# LAW AND EXPLANATION

# Law and Explanation

*An Essay in the Philosophy of Science*

PETER ACHINSTEIN

OXFORD

AT THE CLARENDON PRESS

1971

*Oxford University Press, Ely House, London W. 1*

GLASGOW   NEW YORK   TORONTO   MELBOURNE   WELLINGTON
CAPE TOWN   SALISBURY   IBADAN   NAIROBI   DAR ES SALAAM   LUSAKA   ADDIS ABABA
BOMBAY   CALCUTTA   MADRAS   KARACHI   LAHORE   DACCA
KUALA LUMPUR   SINGAPORE   HONG KONG   TOKYO

PRINTED IN GREAT BRITAIN
AT THE UNIVERSITY PRESS, OXFORD
BY VIVIAN RIDLER
PRINTER TO THE UNIVERSITY

*for Merle Ann*

# Preface

Within the philosophy of science the concept of law has played a prominent role. Various views about explanation, theories, reductionism, determinism, and necessity could not be formulated without it. To explain a phenomenon, on one standard view, is to deduce a statement describing it from a set of propositions containing laws. A scientific theory is often held to be a set of laws with a certain deductive structure. When one science is said to be reducible to another, e.g. chemistry to physics, or when one theory is said to be reducible to another, e.g. geometrical optics to physical optics, such a claim is often analysed to mean that the laws of one science or theory are derivable from those of the other. Determinism, a subject that has exercised philosophers and scientists alike, is a view concerning the existence and nature of laws. There is a theory according to which modal notions such as necessity and possibility are definable by reference to the concept of law.

Whether or not one accepts these theories and analyses—and many do not—it is impossible to deny that the concept of law is one to which philosophers of science often appeal in elaborating their views and in examining the views of others. It is also a concept which has been subjected to scrutiny in its own right. However, the results have not been altogether satisfactory. Confusion exists over what sort of item a law is. Some say that it is a linguistic entity, viz. a sentence, others that it is what a speaker can use a sentence to express, viz. a proposition, and still others that it is a fact of nature which a proposition can describe. Some classify laws as generalizations, while others contrast them with generalizations. Some claim that laws must be universal in the sense of mentioning no particular items or space-time points, while others deny such a claim. Many contrast laws with what they call 'accidental generalizations', claiming that the former but not the latter support counterfactual assertions and can be used in explanations. Others regard such claims as dubious. Again, it is claimed by some but denied by others that scientists discover laws not by inferring them from data but by an act of 'creative imagination', and that inference occurs only after the discovery has been made.

One problem, I think, is that the discussants have been dealing with an extremely broad concept. Examples of laws that are cited include 'Butter melts at 55 °F.' and 'Ravens are black', which no scientist would ever dream of calling laws, along with more standard examples like Newton's laws of motion, the laws of thermodynamics, and Galileo's law. If the term 'law' is to be used this broadly then it is not entirely surprising that disagreements abound. Indeed, one might wonder whether anything really very interesting can be said about so vast and varied a class. I shall not here try to do so. Rather my aim is to examine a narrower concept of law, instances of which will be items that are actually called laws in science. Although scientific terminology is not completely uniform, there are items that one typically finds scientists referring to as laws, others one typically finds scientists never referring to as laws, and still others one finds classified in different ways by different scientists. It is with the former class that I am concerned, and I shall confine my attention to laws in physics and chemistry, since it is here that most examples of the concept are to be found.

Edgar Zilsel, in an important historical study, has pointed out that the concept of law in use today in the sciences is a relatively modern one, first employed in the seventeenth century.[1] Before that time the term 'law' (in its non-juridical sense) was used theistically to refer to the commands God gave to men as well as to the prohibitions he prescribed to the physical world. It was only during the time of Descartes, Boyle, Hooke, and Newton that the term came to be divorced from theological connotations and used in a purely physical sense. One who reads Zilsel's study will find reinforcement for the view that there is a concept of (physical) law in the sciences, and that it is the narrower one to which I referred in the previous paragraph. It remains to be shown that the class of items falling under this concept is of interest for other than historical reasons. But the way to show this is to describe the characteristics of its members and, when appropriate, to discuss these in the light of claims that have been made about laws in the philosophy of science.

Chapter I examines various characteristics of laws in virtue of which

[1] E. Zilsel, 'The Genesis of the Concept of Physical Law', *Philosophical Review*, 51 (1942), 245–79.

they might be said to express regularities. In chapter II my concern is with features of laws which constitute their generality, and in chapter III it is with those features in virtue of which laws might be said to express necessity. Although these chapters focus on certain characteristics of laws that have not been noted or studied sufficiently, they also discuss characteristics traditionally attributed to laws that have been the subject of some attention; for example, I consider the issue of whether, and if so under what conditions, laws can mention particular items, and I discuss the relationship between laws and counterfactual statements. In chapter IV, an attempt is made to provide an analysis of the general concept of explanation, and in chapter V this analysis is applied to the question of the sorts of explanations laws can supply. The final two chapters are concerned with various types of reasoning in which the scientist engages when he proposes a law.

Material for chapter IV, in revised form, was taken from my 'Explanation', *American Philosophical Quarterly* Monograph Series No. 3, and I thank the editor and publisher for permission to use this. In addition I want to express my indebtedness to the U.S. National Science Foundation for research grants, during the tenure of which this book was written, and also to my colleagues Stephen Barker and David Sachs, as well as to students in my graduate seminar in the philosophy of science at The Johns Hopkins University, for stimulating discussions of the issues.

P. A.

*London, 1970*

# Contents

# I. Laws and Regularities

Few philosophers and methodologists of science examine actual scientific laws to determine what characteristics, if any, they share. At best some writers supply conditions for what they call 'lawlike' statements: those, they claim, that would be laws if true. But their examples include propositions which no scientist would ever call laws. My concern is with propositions actually termed laws in science.

I do not claim that the concept of law is precise; scientific terminology does vary. Sometimes 'Equal volumes of all gases at the same pressure and temperature contain the same number of molecules' is called Avogadro's law, sometimes Avogadro's hypothesis. Sometimes the formula $\langle \phi \mid \psi \rangle = \int \langle \phi \mid x \rangle \langle x \mid \psi \rangle \, \mathrm{d}x$ is said to express one of the laws of quantum mechanics, sometimes one of the principles of this subject. This does not necessarily mean that the concept of law is confused, for a proposition may be a law as well as a hypothesis or principle. A law may be called a hypothesis when it is first proposed and not yet tested, or when it is used in contexts in which explicit or implicit reference is made to its (once) untested character. It may be called a principle when it becomes treated as a basic proposition within a scientific subject-matter or theory. There is no incompatibility here. Nevertheless, a tidy set of necessary and sufficient conditions cannot, I think, be produced for laws. The concept has a certain degree of looseness, so that we may have to set down conditions that are relevant and quite central for laws, though not logically necessary. Something might be classifiable as a law even if it failed to satisfy one of them. This sort of looseness is not peculiar to the concept of law, but characterizes many general concepts, such as theory, explanation, and model, which are of concern to the philosopher of science.[1]

One ambiguity in the use of the term 'law' should be noted at the outset. The term is used to refer both to a proposition and to a fact

[1] See my *Concepts of Science* (Baltimore, 1968).

which that proposition describes. When we speak of Newton's law of gravitation we may be referring to the proposition, formulated by Newton, that bodies attract one another with a force directly proportional to their masses and indirectly proportional to the square of the distance between them, or to the fact described. Failure to notice this double use of the term may have been at least partly responsible for the view, held by some philosophers, that laws are not the sort of things which are true or false, something that can be said only of propositions not facts. Employing the term in the propositional sense, we can say that Bode's law—the proposition formulated by Johann Elert Bode in 1772, which says that the radius of the orbit of any planet, in astronomical units, is $R = 0.3 \times 2^{(n-2)} + 0.4$—is false as it stands. Alternatively, we can say that there is no such law, meaning that what is described by that proposition is not a fact.

Laws are sometimes contrasted with generalizations.[1] For example, it might be said, 'Gases combine in simple ratios by volume' is a law (Gay-Lussac's law), whereas 'Mammals manufacture their own vitamin C' is a generalization. If there is a difference between these two cases it is not one I should refer to as law as opposed to generalization. Something is a generalization if it was arrived at, and possibly justified by, generalizing from instances or cases. Now there are laws that fit such a description, and Gay-Lussac's law is one of them. As we shall see in chapter VII, Gay-Lussac arrived at his law and justified it by generalizing from the combining ratios of particular gases. Another example is the second law of thermodynamics. The proposition that no system operating in a cycle can transfer heat from one body to another at a higher temperature without work being done on the system by the surroundings can be described as a broad generalization from experience, from observation of various types of processes that do and do not occur. Law and generalization are not mutually exclusive categories.

## 1. Laws express Regularities

How, then, can we characterize the concept of law? Let us begin with some typical propositions actually classified as laws:

Every body continues in its state of rest, or of uniform motion in a right line, unless it is compelled to change that state by forces impressed upon it (Newton's first law of motion).

---

[1] See S. Toulmin, *Philosophy of Science* (London, 1953), p. 99.

The radiation emitted by black bodies is such that its intensity per second per unit area of the body is proportional to the fourth power of the absolute temperature of the body (Stefan–Boltzmann law).

The mass of an element liberated or deposited on entering into reaction at an electrode during electrolysis is proportional to the quantity of electricity passing (Faraday's first law of electrolysis).

Charged particles exert a force on one another that varies inversely with the square of the distance between them (Coulomb's law).

Each of these is concerned with the behaviour of objects or substances, i.e. with their actions, interactions, or changes under certain conditions. What sort of concern with behaviour do these laws manifest? They describe some regularity in behaviour. Their concern is with the manner in which an item regularly acts, interacts, or changes, rather than with its behaviour on some particular occasion, and with all items of certain sorts rather than with particular ones (this will be elaborated further in chapter II on generality). Newton's first law describes all bodies subject to no external forces as regularly remaining at rest or moving with uniform velocity in a straight line; the Stefan–Boltzmann law describes all black bodies as regularly emitting radiation of a certain type.

However, not every proposition describing a regularity in behaviour is a law. Some propositions attributing properties to items can be said to describe regularities in behaviour, yet they are not laws, e.g. 'All copper melts when heated to 1,980 °F.'. Moreover, although the laws I have cited above are typical of a large class, there are others that one might be reluctant to characterize as describing behaviour, since no items appear to be described as acting, interacting, or changing. The law of Dulong and Petit states that the product of the atomic weight of a solid element multiplied by its specific heat is a constant. Avogadro's law states that equal volumes of all gases at the same pressure and temperature contain the same number of molecules. Gauss's law states that the flux of the electric field through a surface is proportional to the charge inside the surface. To be sure, in some of these cases it is possible to reformulate the law in such a way that it makes a statement about the actions, interactions, or changes of objects or substances. (Gauss's law can be formulated so as to describe the action of charges within a surface of a body on points on the surface.) But in other cases, as with Avogadro's law, such reformulations would be strained or impossible. In any event, what is important in these cases is the idea of regularity. Laws describe a regularity, which often can be said to be a regularity in the way objects or substances behave, but sometimes is better described simply as a regularity in the properties or characteristics that certain objects or substances exhibit. This regularity consists in the fact that (1) under certain conditions there is always certain behaviour or the occurrence of certain properties, and (2) this behaviour or these properties are exhibited by all objects of certain types.

To say this much, however, is not to go very far, since we need to know the manner or respects in which laws describe such regularities. For example, each of the following propositions describes a regularity, although neither is a law: All bodies fall when unsupported; all light rays are refracted when entering a medium of different optical density. Yet each is a near-law. We need only say: All bodies fall when unsupported in such a way that the distance traversed is proportional to the square of the time (Galileo's law); all light rays are refracted when entering a medium of different optical density in such a way that the ratio of the sine of the angle of incidence to the sine of the angle of refraction is a constant (Snell's law).

Accordingly, it is tempting to say that laws are concerned with the *quantitative* aspects of a regularity, or even that they are simply formulae. Such a view might be encouraged by noting that in textbooks laws are frequently presented as formulae:

$$(1) \quad s = \tfrac{1}{2}gt^2 \qquad \text{(Galileo's law)},$$

$$(2) \quad \frac{\sin i}{\sin r} = n \qquad \text{(Snell's law)}.$$

Whether or not we identify a particular law as a formula (assuming now that there is a formula with which it is associated) depends on how much interpretation we build into the symbols of the formula. For example, in (2) if we interpret $i$ as the angle of incidence of a light ray entering a medium of a different optical density, and $r$ as the angle of refraction of the ray which proceeds through this medium, then (2) can be identified as more or less completely expressing the proposition or fact that is Snell's law. On the other hand, if $i$ is interpreted simply as angle of incidence and $r$ as angle of refraction, then Snell's law is more adequately identified as the proposition or fact that light rays are refracted when entering a medium of different optical density in such a way that formula (2) is satisfied. Furthermore, if we say that laws are concerned with the quantitative aspects of a regularity what shall we say about laws that seem to be non-

quantitative, laws that lack a formula? The second law of thermo
dynamics, as formulated on p. 2, is such a law. I shall hold this
question in abeyance for the moment, and in what follows propose
four characteristics that are typical of laws, the regularities they
express, and their manner of expressing them.

## 2. Four Characteristics of Laws

To introduce the first let us begin with a simple example, Boyle's law,
and consider the sort of experiment Boyle himself performed. He
prepared a glass J-tube [Fig. 1] sealing off the short
leg and leaving the long leg open. Into the long leg
he poured mercury until the mercury level was the
same in both legs. Then he slowly poured more
mercury into the long leg, noting at various intervals
the level in each leg. He recorded his data in a table,
the first column of which gives the distance between the
top of the short leg and the mercury level in that leg,
the second column the amount of mercury added to
the long leg, the third column the number $29\frac{1}{8}$, the
fourth column the addition of numbers in the second
and third columns. (The fifth column I will explain
presently.) Some of the entries look like this:

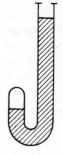

FIG. 1.

| A | B | C | D | E |
|---|---|---|---|---|
| 48 | 00 | $29\frac{1}{8}$ | $29\frac{2}{16}$ | $29\frac{2}{16}$ |
| 46 | $01\frac{7}{16}$ | $29\frac{1}{8}$ | $30\frac{9}{16}$ | $30\frac{6}{16}$ |
| 24 | $29\frac{11}{16}$ | $29\frac{1}{8}$ | $58\frac{13}{16}$ | $58\frac{2}{8}$ |
| 12 | $88\frac{7}{16}$ | $29\frac{1}{8}$ | $117\frac{9}{16}$ | $116\frac{4}{8}$ |

What does this mean? By adding mercury to the long leg, Boyle was
increasing the pressure on the air in the short leg; he was compressing
the air. Now the standard atmospherical pressure, as measured in
inches of mercury, is $29\frac{1}{8}$. This is the figure used in column C which
must be added to the figure in B to determine the total pressure on
the air in the short leg. Examining the figures we see that when the
volume of air in the short leg is decreased to one half its original
value, the pressure on it and hence its pressure is increased to
(approximately) double its original value; when the volume is
decreased to a quarter of its original value, the pressure of the air
is quadrupled. There is a regularity here, and it is expressed by Boyle's
law, which says that the pressure and volume of a gas are inversely

proportional, symbolically: $p \propto 1/V$. Column E expresses what, using this law, the pressure should be if the volume is as given in column A.

Notice that column D of the table gives results in inches of mercury added to the long leg$+29\frac{1}{8}$, and column A in inches between the mercury and the top of the short leg. We might say that there is a regular connection between the height of the mercury in the long leg and the distance between the mercury and the top of the short leg, but this is not Boyle's law. Boyle's law gets behind this regularity to the more fundamental one between pressure and volume of air. This is more fundamental in the sense that it can be used to analyse and explain the regularity exhibited in the table. When we employ Boyle's law we can say that what the figures in the table show is that the pressure of the air is inversely proportional to its volume, and that the reason why the distance between the mercury and the top of the short leg varies with the height of the mercury in the long leg is that the air in the short leg is being compressed by the addition of mercury to the long leg. It is because of this fundamental regularity that changes in column D are inversely proportional to those in column A.

Generalizing, I would say that a law (construed in the propositional sense) expresses, or purports to express, a regularity that underlies some other less fundamental regularity or regularities, i.e. one that can be used to analyse and explain these other regularities. We use a law to analyse a less fundamental regularity by identifying certain aspects of that regularity employing concepts of the law and by showing how the law is exemplified in that regularity. In our example we analyse the less fundamental regularity involving columns of mercury by identifying the distance between the mercury and top of the short leg as giving the volume of the air in the short leg and the inches of mercury added to the long leg$+29\frac{1}{8}$ as giving the pressure of the air in the short leg, and then by indicating that what the figures show is that the pressure and volume of the air are inversely proportional. It is this regularity that is exemplified in the regularity exhibited in columns A and D of the table. We use a law to explain a less fundamental regularity by using it to answer certain types of questions, including, among others, 'What underlying regularity is exemplified?' (The nature of explanation, as well as the issue of what sorts of explanations laws supply, will be examined in chapters IV and V.) In our example Boyle's law can be appealed to in explaining why the distance between the mercury and the top of the short leg varies with the height of the mercury in the long leg and why they are inversely related.

Consider some other examples. Newton in expounding his first law of motion notes the regularity that projectiles continue in their motions so far as they are not retarded by the resistance of the air or by gravity. He also notes that when a top is spun its parts are 'drawn aside from rectilinear motions' by the force of cohesion, and that the top eventually slows down because of air resistance. There are many other regularities that could be cited: people in a moving train tend to lurch forward when the train suddenly stops or decelerates; passengers in a car slide to the left of the car when a sudden right turn is made; a puck when hit on the ice moves in a straight line and the smoother the ice the farther it moves. The more fundamental regularity that can be appealed to in analysing and explaining each of these is expressed by the law that every body continues in its state of rest, or of uniform motion in a straight line, unless compelled to change that state by forces impressed on it. The projectile, a material body, exhibits uniform and rectilinear motion unless the air exerts a force on it or gravity does. The parts of the top would proceed with uniform motion in a straight line if it were not for the forces of cohesion between these parts. People in a moving train tend to lurch forward when the train stops because they were previously moving in a forward direction and no force was impressed upon them when the train stopped. In each case the regularity is analysed and explained by using concepts such as material body, uniform motion, rectilinear motion, and force, and by invoking Newton's law.

Or consider the first law of thermodynamics, which can be expressed by introducing the following definitions. Work is said to be done by a system during a given process if the sole effect external to the system could be reduced to the rise of a weight. Heat in thermodynamics is said to be transferred between two systems in virtue of a difference in temperature between them. The internal energy of a thermodynamic system is the total energy of the system minus its kinetic energy of visible motion and its gravitational potential energy. Using these concepts the first law of thermodynamics can be expressed by saying that the difference between the internal energies of any two states of a system is equal to the difference between the heat absorbed and the external work done in getting from one state to the other. This law can be used to analyse various regularities. If, e.g., a fluid is enclosed in a cylinder by a piston on which there rests a block, and the fluid is heated, it expands, causing the piston to rise. Using the first law of thermodynamics we can analyse this regularity by identifying the fluid as a thermodynamic system that is under constant pressure from the block and is such that when it is heated work is performed by the system (since there is a rise of a weight). In order to apply the first law to this system we can rewrite the law in mathematical terms like this: $dU = đQ - đW$, where $U =$ internal energy, $Q =$ heat, and $W =$ work. If we neglect any friction and turbulence we can treat the above process as reversible and use the relationship $đW = p \, dV$, where $p =$ pressure and $V =$ volume. Using the first law expressed as above we can then obtain the following relationship which holds for this process: $đQ = d(U+pV)$, where $U+pV$ ($= H =$ enthalpy) is a thermodynamic property of a system in the sense that it has a definite numerical value when the system is in a particular state, and this value is independent of the process through which the system passed to reach that state. Accordingly, the regularity exhibited can be analysed by using the first law of thermodynamics and saying that what we have here is a constant pressure process in which heat is transferred in an amount equal to the change in enthalpy. And the first law can be invoked in explaining various aspects of the regularity, e.g. why the heat transferred depends only on the initial and final values of the internal energy, pressure, and volume of the fluid and not on intermediate values.

In all of these cases the analysis and explanation of a given regularity or set of regularities is accomplished by employing certain concepts under which items involved in the less fundamental regularities can be classified and related. In the case of Boyle's law, the J-tube containing mercury in both legs is classifiable as a system containing a gas which assumes different pressures and volumes. In the case of Newton's first law, people, projectiles, and pucks are all classifiable as material bodies capable of uniform rectilinear motion and also capable of being subjected to unbalanced forces. In the case of the first law of thermodynamics, a fluid that is heated and that is contained in a cylinder with a movable piston is classifiable as a thermodynamic system which does work, in which heat flows, and which can experience changes in internal energy and enthalpy. The concepts employed in a law are typically more general than those used to describe the less fundamental regularities, and they are ones in terms of which various aspects of such regularities are explained. This is not to say that when a scientist discovers or attempts to justify a law he always reasons to the law on the basis of the fact that it is capable of analysing and explaining regularities. As we shall see in chapter VII, this happens sometimes but not always. My point here is only that laws express regularities that can be cited in providing analyses and explanations of the sort described.

The analyses and explanations are physical ones and not solely mathematical or formal. To illustrate this contrast consider the following example. In 1885, Johann Jakob Balmer published a formula relating the wavelengths of the lines of the hydrogen spectrum. Previously, Ångström had provided measurements of these four lines, and what Balmer did was note that if $m^2/(m^2-n^2)$, where $m$ and $n$ are whole numbers, is multiplied by $h = 3645 \cdot 6$ mm/$10^7$, this will give wavelengths of the first four lines very close to those measured by Ångström. Balmer presents the following table for the series with $n = 2$:

| According to Balmer formula | | | Ångström gives | Difference |
|---|---|---|---|---|
| $H_\alpha$ | (*C*-line) | $= \frac{9}{5}h = 6562 \cdot 08$ | $6562 \cdot 10$ | $+0 \cdot 02$ |
| $H_\beta$ | (*F*-line) | $= \frac{4}{3}h = 4860 \cdot 8$ | $4860 \cdot 74$ | $-0 \cdot 06$ |
| $H_\gamma$ | (near *G*) | $= \frac{25}{21}h = 4340 \cdot 0$ | $4340 \cdot 1$ | $+0 \cdot 1$ |
| $H_\delta$ | (*h*-line) | $= \frac{9}{8}h = 4101 \cdot 3$ | $4101 \cdot 2$ | $-0 \cdot 1$ |

Balmer's formula was even used to predict new lines which were later discovered and found to be close in value to those predicted by the formula. Generally speaking, this formula is not called a law, and it is of interest to speculate why not. What is the difference between this formula and Boyle's law, for example?

Both Boyle and Balmer present tables comparing observed values of a quantity with the values predicted in accordance with a formula. The difference consists in the fact that Balmer's formula, unlike Boyle's law, supplies no physical analysis or explanation of the data. Balmer simply gives us the constant $h = 3645 \cdot 6$ mm/$10^7$ and tells us to multiply it by an algebraic schema $m^2/(m^2-n^2)$, for whose variables $m$ and $n$ we are to substitute numbers. If we do so we will obtain the wavelengths of the hydrogen lines. But the formula does not say how the lines are produced or why they have the wavelengths they do. It simply provides a device for calculating the numerical values of the lines. We might say that it provides a numerical, but not a physical, analysis of Ångström's data. Boyle, on the other hand, analyses and explains the data (the recorded values in the heights of mercury columns) by introducing the physical ideas of pressure, volume, and compressibility of a gas. Both physicists discovered a regularity in the data, but only Boyle provided an analysis and explanation of the data in physical terms.

So far I have said that laws purport to express a more fundamental regularity various regularities may exemplify. There are three related characteristics that must be mentioned if we are to understand how this regularity is to be expressed. One, which should be evident from what has already been said, is that laws attempt to express the more fundamental regularity with a certain amount of completeness by isolating the various factors that are involved and indicating the manner in which they are related. It is not enough to say simply that all unsupported bodies fall; the law describes the manner of the fall: the fact that the distance fallen depends upon the time and how it depends on this. A radiation law will not say simply that all black bodies emit radiation, but will attempt to say what the amount of radiation emitted depends upon (the temperature of the body) and the nature of the dependence. One of the ways in which a law provides an analysis and explanation of regularities is by identifying and relating those factors common to them. Boyle's law analyses and explains the regularities exhibited in the heights of mercury columns by isolating the factors of pressure and volume of air that are involved and indicating that they are inversely related. The present feature of laws is one that distinguishes them from many other propositions in science which, like 'All unsupported bodies fall', even if they can be said to express regularities, do not isolate and relate factors that are involved in the regularities or do so very incompletely.

Another characteristic of laws is that they attempt to formulate a regularity in a precise manner. The concepts employed are generally technical ones with precise meanings, and the relationships are often, though not always, described quantitatively. Ordinary notions, such as that of something getting hotter when rubbed, may be replaced by more specialized ones, such as the thermodynamic concepts of work and heat, and the relationships between them may be described mathematically by the use of a formula. What is precision? In a general way, it has to do with the recognition or use of sharply defined boundaries. A term is precisely defined if it is defined in such a way that the items or situations to or in which it is and is not applicable can be sharply delimited even when small differences exist between them. Quantitative concepts are precise ones since their use is based upon a numerical scale permitting small differences in degree to be sharply distinguished. Laws are precise in that they are often formulated using such concepts.

Earlier I noted the temptation to say that laws are concerned with quantitative aspects of regularities and even that they are simply formulae, a temptation that perhaps ought to be resisted, since a formula need not always be involved in the formulation of a law, and even when it is, the formula need not always be interpreted as fully expressing the law. Nevertheless, there is a tendency to attempt to restate laws first formulated qualitatively in a quantitative way. Clausius, e.g., after stating the second law of thermodynamics in the form 'Heat cannot of itself pass from a colder to a hotter body', proceeds to a quantitative treatment of this law. Introducing the concept of entropy, designated by the letter $S$, he formulates this law using the formula $dQ = T\,dS$. The quantitative formulation of a law adds precision to its statement. It also allows the scientist to employ mathematical techniques for deriving theorems, making predictions, and relating it to other laws. Quantitative formulations of the first and second laws of thermodynamics permit the physicist to express both laws using one mathematically tractable formula:

$$T\,dS = dU + p\,dV.$$

The final characteristic I want to note here is simplicity. The scientist seeks not only to isolate various factors involved in a regularity and to formulate the regularity in a precise manner, but also to provide a simple formulation of it. There are several criteria of simplicity in the case of laws, one of which concerns the number of different factors or terms the law contains. Galileo's law of freely falling bodies isolates three factors: the time of the fall, the distance fallen, and the gravitational constant. It ignores the force on the body due to air resistance. There are more complex formulae which take this into account but introduce new terms. For example, it may be assumed that the air resistance is proportional to the first power of the velocity, in which case a constant of proportionality in addition to the gravitational constant is needed.

Another criterion of simplicity concerns the nature of the terms or factors that are included. Are they 'primitive' ones within the science, or are they given definitions by reference to others, and if so, how complex are these definitions? The law of the simple pendulum states that the period $T$ is related to the length $l$ by the formula

$$T = 2\pi(l/g)^{\frac{1}{2}},$$

where $g$ is the gravitational constant. Compare this with the equation for the simple harmonic oscillator: $T = 2\pi(I/Mgd)^{\frac{1}{2}}$, where $I$ = rotational inertia of the body about an axis through a point $P$, $M$ = mass of oscillator, and $d$ = distance between $P$ and the centre of mass of the body. One aspect of this which makes it more complex than the law of the simple pendulum is that it contains the term $I$ for rotational inertia. In mechanics this receives a complex definition as the sum of the products of the masses of the particles of the body by the squares of their respective distances from the axis of rotation. The only (non-constant) term on the right-hand side of the simple pendulum equation is the term for length, one of the fundamental terms in mechanics.

A third criterion of simplicity in laws concerns the complexity of the relationship between the terms which the law postulates. This is especially evident when a law is formulated mathematically. The mathematical relationship between distance and time is simpler in Galileo's law than in statements which take into account air resistance. Galileo's law states that the distance fallen $s$ is related to the time $t$ by the formula $s = \frac{1}{2}gt^2$. A more complex relationship, postulated by a statement taking air resistance into account, is

$$s = \tfrac{1}{2}gt^2 - \tfrac{1}{6}gkt^3,$$

which relates the distance to the square of the time and also to the cube of the time.

The quest for simplicity sometimes conflicts with the quest for completeness. When the scientist seeks to formulate a law, because he is pulled toward simplicity, he may ignore certain factors involved in the regularity. In some cases he is aware of these, in others not. Galileo was aware that his law ignored air resistance, Boyle was not aware that his law ignored the rotation of molecules as well as intermolecular attractive forces. Even if it is not known what factors are being ignored the scientist may realize that such factors exist when he determines that the law, as he has formulated it, gives results that are not completely accurate.[1] If those who use such a law realize that it does ignore factors they will treat it as an idealization, i.e. as something holding under conditions in which such factors are not present. Galileo's law will be treated as an idealization holding when a body falls in a vacuum; Boyle's law as an idealization holding for gases composed of mass-point molecules which do not exhibit forces of attraction.

[1] This feature of laws is one that has been emphasized by M. Scriven, 'The Key Property of Physical Laws—Inaccuracy', *Current Issues in the Philosophy of Science*, ed. H. Feigl and G. Maxwell (New York, 1961), pp. 91–101.

Subsequently, scientists usually seek to formulate more complex propositions that do take these factors into consideration and as a result are more accurate. Quite often these propositions will not themselves be called laws. Boyle's law, which contains the formula $pV = $ const., is less accurate than the so-called virial equations, one of which can be expressed as $pV = A+Bp+Cp^2+Dp^3$, where $A$, $B$, $C$, $D$ depend on the temperature and the mass of the gas. The ideal-gas law, which relates pressure, temperature, and volume, by saying that $pV = RT$, is less accurate than van der Waals's equation $(p+a/V^2)(V-b) = RT$ which takes into consideration the presence of intermolecular attractive forces (in the term $a/V^2$) and the finite size of the molecules (in the $b$-term). Van der Waals's equation may itself be replaced by the more accurate virial equation

$$pV = RT+Ap+Bp^2+Cp^3,$$

in which $A$, $B$, $C$ are functions of temperature. The reason why such formulae are not usually called laws may be because they are more complex, in several of the respects noted, than the corresponding propositions which are generally classified as laws.[1]

## 3. Varied Formulations of Laws

Let me summarize the characteristics of laws so far discussed. (They are characteristics of laws construed as propositions, but we can also speak of laws as facts described by such propositions.)

(1) Laws express, or purport to express, regularities underlying other regularities in such a way that the latter can be analysed and explained in physical terms by the former.

(2) Laws express, or purport to express, regularities with a certain amount of completeness by isolating various factors that are involved and indicating the manner in which they are related.

(3) Laws express, or purport to express, regularities in a precise manner, frequently using technical concepts with precise meanings, and they are often formulated quantitatively.

(4) Laws express, or purport to express, simple regularities, where simplicity is a function of the number and kinds of terms or factors

---

[1] In some cases, however, the more complex propositions are called laws. Planck's radiation law is less simple, though considerably more accurate, than the Rayleigh–Jeans law. These laws state that the energy of wavelength $\lambda$ emitted by a black body is related to the temperature of the body as follows:

$$\psi_\lambda = \frac{8\pi kT}{\lambda^4} \text{ (Rayleigh–Jeans)}; \qquad \psi_\lambda = \frac{8\pi ch}{\lambda^5} \frac{1}{e^{ch/\lambda kT}-1} \text{ (Planck)}.$$

the law contains and the relationships between them which the law postulates.

How much analysis and explanation a law provides, how completely it analyses regularities, how precise and how simple it is, will vary to some extent from one law to another. We must also recognize that one law can have several formulations (i.e. several propositions may be said to express that law), and some of these will be more precise than others, some more complete, some more capable of providing deeper analyses and explanations, and some simpler. The formulations may even include different concepts. One formulation of the second law of thermodynamics is this:

$L_1$: No system operating in a cycle can transfer heat from one body to another at a higher temperature without work being done on the system by the surroundings.

Another is this:

$L_2$: It is impossible to construct a system which, operating in a cycle, will produce no other effect than the extraction of heat from a single heat reservoir and the performance of an equivalent amount of work.

Still another is this:

$L_3$: There exists a property $S$ (= entropy) of a system such that a change in its value is equal to $S_2 - S_1 = \int_1^2 dQ/T$ for any reversible process undergone by the system between states 1 and 2.

The first formulation expresses a fact underlying the regularity that no refrigerator cools objects by conveying heat from them 'at no cost'. However, by the introduction of the concepts of a cycle, temperature, and work, the law expresses the underlying regularity in a more fundamental way, more completely, and more precisely. The third formulation provides a quantitative expression of the law and introduces concepts not present in the first two.

Different formulations of a law may or may not be logically or mathematically equivalent. Galileo's law, expressed as 'All unsupported bodies fall with uniform acceleration', can be shown to be mathematically equivalent to the formulation 'All unsupported bodies fall in such a way that the distance fallen is proportional to the square of the time'. By contrast, formulations $L_1$ and $L_2$ of the second law of thermodynamics given above are not logically or mathematically equivalent. Their equivalence is demonstrated by showing that if there is a violation of one there is a violation of the other, but in order to show this additional empirical assumptions must be made. Let us consider the case in which if there is a violation of formulation $L_1$ there is a violation of $L_2$. Suppose, contrary to $L_1$, that there exists a system, a heat pump, which operates in a cycle in such a way as to transfer say 10 B.T.U. of heat from a body of lower temperature $T_2$ to a body of higher temperature $T_1$ without receiving work from the surroundings. This is shown diagrammatically in Fig. 2. We now

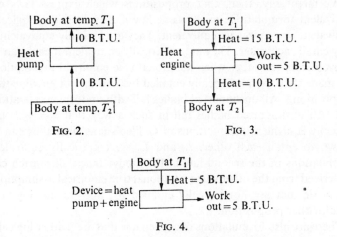

FIG. 2.                                    FIG. 3.

FIG. 4.

suppose that there is a heat engine operating in a cycle in such a way that it takes in 15 B.T.U. from the body at temperature $T_1$, produces the equivalent of 5 B.T.U. of work, and rejects 10 B.T.U. to the second body at temperature $T_2$, shown in Fig. 3. If the heat pump and the heat engine are coupled together the 10 B.T.U. going into and out of the body at $T_2$ cancel and there is no net heat transfer into this body. The over-all result is illustrated in Fig. 4. The device consisting of the heat pump and heat engine transfers heat from a single source completely into work, and this violates formulation $L_2$ of the second law.

What is thus shown is that if it is physically possible for a device to exist that violates formulation $L_1$ then it is physically possible for a device to exist that violates formulation $L_2$. Note, however, that the proof requires two assumptions in addition to the assumption that it is physically possible for a device to exist violating $L_1$. One is that it is physically possible for there to exist a device, a heat engine, which can take in heat from one body, produce work, and reject a certain amount of heat to a second body. Another is that it is physically possible for a device to exist which couples a heat engine with a heat pump. Both of these are empirical assumptions, and neither is logically entailed by the assumption that it is physically possible for a device to exist that violates $L_1$. The two formulations of the second law can be derived from each other provided that additional empirical assumptions are made. They are not logically equivalent.

We might say, then, that propositions which express laws are equivalent formulations of the same law if they are either logically equivalent or empirically equivalent. They are logically equivalent if they entail each other. They are empirically equivalent if each can be derived from the other when additional true empirical assumptions are made that are not logically entailed by, and do not entail, either proposition.[1] 'All unsupported bodies fall with uniform acceleration' and 'All unsupported bodies fall in such a way that $s = \frac{1}{2}gt^2$' are logically equivalent formulations of Galileo's law, since they can be shown to entail each other. $L_1$ and $L_2$ are empirically equivalent formulations of the second law of thermodynamics, since each can be derived from the other when additional true empirical assumptions are made that are not logically entailed by, and do not logically entail, either proposition.

There are also formulations of a given law that are neither logically nor empirically equivalent. I shall call these non-equivalent formulations. For example, Coulomb originally formulated his electrical law as follows: 'The repulsive force between two small spheres charged with the same type of electricity is inversely proportional to the square of the distance between the centres of the two spheres.' This is different from certain later non-equivalent formulations in two respects. It does not mention that the force is proportional to the product of the strengths of the charges, and it is restricted to forces between like charges, whereas more general formulations allow forces between unlike charges as well. Here then are two ways in which formulations of a law may differ. One may be more complete than the other in virtue of including more factors involved in the regularity; one may

[1] In this definition the additional empirical assumptions will not be permitted to be simple truth-functional compounds, since otherwise any two laws would be empirically equivalent. For suppose that $p$ is true and that $p$ entails $L_2$. Then the truth-functional compound $L_1 \supset p$ is true, and this, together with $L_1$, entails $L_2$, and by itself it is not entailed by and does not entail $L_1$ or $L_2$. A similar manœuvre could be made with $L_2 \supset q$, where $q$ is true and entails $L_1$, and this would show that $L_1$ and $L_2$ are empirically equivalent.

be more general than the other in virtue of attributing the regularity to a more general subject. There are other respects in which non-equivalent formulations can differ. One may be more precise than another. Instead of formulating the law of conservation of energy as 'Energy is indestructible', which is quite vague, thermodynamics seeks a precise formulation in terms of the concepts of heat, work, and internal energy of a thermodynamic system. Another way in which formulations can differ is if one imposes certain restrictions on the subject exhibiting the regularity which the other does not. According to Boyle's original formulation of his law, gases are such that their pressure and volume are inversely proportional. According to a more restricted formulation gases *at constant temperature* exhibit this regularity.

When are two non-equivalent propositions formulations of the same law and when are they formulations of different laws? Why do we want to say, e.g., that 'All gases at constant temperature are such that $p \propto 1/V$' is a formulation of Boyle's law that is more qualified than Boyle's original formulation, whereas 'All gases are such that $(p+a/V^2)(V-b) = RT$' is not a more qualified formulation of the ideal gas law 'All gases are such that $pV = RT$'? The answer seems to be that a sufficient condition for regarding two propositions as formulations of different laws, or at least not as formulations of the same law, is that the regularities they ascribe to items are incompatible.[1] A gas's behaving in such a way that $(p+a/V^2)(V-b) = RT$ is not compatible with its behaving in such a way that $pV = RT$. Accordingly, the proposition that gases obey the former equation is not a formulation of the ideal-gas law. On the other hand, differences in generality of subjects exhibiting the regularity, or differences in restrictions imposed on the subjects, do not, by themselves, suffice to make the propositions formulations of different laws or prevent them from being formulations of the same law. Nor do differences in completeness of factors isolated, or in the precision with which the law is formulated, unless the resulting regularities attributed are incompatible.

If various equivalent as well as non-equivalent propositions can be formulations of one and the same law, then, it might be asked, how

---

[1] This criterion is more accurately stated in terms of concepts to be introduced in the next chapter, by saying that two propositions with the same subject term are formulations of different laws, or at least not formulations of the same law, if their consequent conditions are incompatible.

can a law be construed as a proposition? Shouldn't we say that a law is a set of propositions? What I said earlier was that when someone refers to a law he may be referring to a proposition, and this is true whether or not there are varied formulations of a law. There are several propositions that scientists refer to by the label 'the law of conservation of energy'. Each may be called the law of conservation of energy. This label does not, of course, apply to the set of these collectively but to members of that set. This means that the use of what is normally a singular referring expression, 'the so and so', is potentially misleading in the case of laws, although in any given context in which it is used a particular proposition may be what is being referred to.

So far I have considered characteristics of laws relating to the idea that laws express regularities. I have concentrated on the fact that these regularities underlie others for which they provide a physical analysis and explanation, on features of completeness, precision, and simplicity with which laws are expressed, as well as on the fact that varied formulations are possible. In the two chapters that follow I turn to several other characteristics of laws; these pertain to the ideas of generality and necessity.

# II. The Generality of Laws

## 1. A Subject of a Law

Generality is of the essence of a law, that is quite obvious. What is not so obvious is how this concept can be defined. In chapter I, I said that a law describes a regularity. To what sort of item can this regularity be attributed? Unfortunately, there is no simple answer to this question. The chemical law of mass action states that at constant temperature the rate of a chemical reaction is directly proportional to the concentration of each of the reacting substances. We might say that this law attributes a regularity to the rate of a chemical reaction, to chemical reactions themselves, or to chemical reactants. More generally, regularities described by a law might be attributed to substances or objects, i.e. to items, such as electricity and radiation, denoted by 'mass' nouns, or to items, such as particles and planets, denoted by 'count' nouns, as well as to items, like gases and chemical reactants, denoted by nouns that can be treated in both ways. But regularities might also be attributed to properties, processes, phenomena, and states associated with these substances or objects. In what follows, in order to permit a perspicuous way of viewing the generality of laws, I shall employ the categories of substance and object to introduce the idea of a *subject* of a law. In so doing I assume that items in these categories are ones, but not necessarily the only ones, to which a regularity expressed by a law can be ascribed.

By a subject of a law I mean whatever objects or substances it is or is supposed to be (a) that could be said to exhibit a regularity described by the law, (b) that would be investigated in testing the law, and (c) to which the regularity noted in (a) could reasonably be attributed as a property or characteristic. If the fact that an item possesses $P$, given that it possesses certain other properties, would count at least to some extent in favour of concluding that it is an item of type $X$, and if the fact that it lacks $P$ would count to some extent against this conclusion, then I shall say that $P$ can reasonably be attributed as a property or characteristic to an item of type $X$.[1] Planets and gases satisfy the appropriate conditions for being subjects of Kepler's first law and of Boyle's law, respectively. Planets are objects that exhibit the regularity of revolving around the sun in elliptical orbits, that would be investigated in testing Kepler's law, and to which the above regularity described by the law could reasonably be attributed as a property or characteristic in the sense I have indicated. Gases are substances satisfying conditions (a), (b), and (c) with respect to Boyle's law. These are examples of subjects that are groups, but a subject might also be a single substance of a given type which satisfies the above conditions, such as electricity or light.

The notion of a subject of a law should be understood as relativized to a given proposition, i.e. to some particular formulation of that law, even though in many cases the same item can be taken to be a subject of different formulations. With respect to a particular formulation, in some cases there will be only one reasonable choice for a subject, or at least one choice more reasonable than others, but in other cases this will not be so. Black bodies or black-body radiation might equally well be taken to be a subject of the Stefan–Boltzmann law, expressed as: 'The radiation emitted by black bodies is such that its intensity per second per unit area of the body is proportional to the fourth power of the absolute temperature of the body.' The law describes a regularity in the behaviour of objects called black bodies as well as in the behaviour of the substance called black-body radiation, both of these would be investigated in testing the law, and the law could reasonably be said to be ascribing properties or characteristics to both. When the notion of subject is used in what follows, what is said is meant to hold for all items that could reasonably be classified as subjects of a law.

Two restrictions will be made, however. On the present criterion we could say, for example, that a subject of Galileo's law is unsupported bodies and the regularity is falling with uniform acceleration; we could also speak of bodies as a subject and say that the regularity is falling with uniform acceleration if unsupported. In such cases I shall designate only the more general type of object, in this instance bodies, as subject, and speak of being unsupported as an antecedent condition that bodies are supposed to satisfy. Let me make this more

---

[1] In *Concepts of Science*, pp. 6 ff., this is what I call a property relevant for being an $X$.

precise. Suppose that with respect to a given formulation of a law both $S_1$ and $S_2$ could reasonably be said to satisfy conditions (a), (b), and (c) for being a subject of that law. Suppose further that being an $S_1$ logically entails being an $S_2$ but not conversely. Then $S_2$ may be taken to be more general than $S_1$. Suppose that with respect to the same formulation of that law there is no $S_3$ that also could reasonably be said to satisfy conditions (a), (b), and (c) and that is more general than $S_2$ in the sense just indicated. Then $S_2$ can be designated as a subject of the law but $S_1$ cannot. Since being an $S_1$ logically entails being an $S_2$ but not conversely, and since $S_1$ and $S_2$ both satisfy conditions (a), (b), and (c), it should be apparent that being an $S_1$ is tantamount to being an $S_2$ that satisfies some further condition, which I call an antecedent condition. (Being an unsupported body $S_1$ is tantamount to being a body $S_2$ that satisfies the antecedent condition of being unsupported.)

I shall also speak of the consequent condition which a subject, or a subject satisfying an antecedent condition, is supposed to satisfy. If there is an antecedent condition, then a regularity expressed by the law is characterized by items that satisfy a subject term satisfying the consequent condition when they satisfy the antecedent condition; otherwise it is characterized simply by their satisfying the consequent condition. In Galileo's law the consequent condition can be taken to be 'falling with uniform acceleration'. In Snell's law 'entering a medium of a different optical density' can be taken to be an antecedent condition which light rays, the subject, are supposed to satisfy; 'being refracted in accordance with the rule $\sin i/\sin r = \text{const.}$' would then be the consequent condition. Since it may be possible to treat more than one item as a subject of a law, what is designated as antecedent and consequent conditions can vary. As with subjects, what is said in what follows about a given law is meant to hold for all conditions that could reasonably be classified as antecedent and consequent conditions of that law.

The need for a second restriction derives from the fact that some laws mention particular objects that might be taken to satisfy conditions (a), (b), and (c) for subjects. Kepler's first law mentions the sun, a particular object, and attributes to it the characteristic of being at one focus of an ellipse which is the path of each planet. In such cases I shall take as a subject not the particular object that is mentioned but objects or substances of a more general type that bear certain relationships to the particular one. In Kepler's first law this would be planets, and the sun would be mentioned in the consequent condition.

When I say that a subject of a law should be understood as relativized to a particular formulation, I do not mean that it must be explicitly mentioned in that formulation. Without explicit mention certain objects or substances might be said to exhibit a regularity described by a law, be investigated in testing the law, and be such that the regularity is attributable to them as a property or characteristic. The second law of thermodynamics is sometimes stated by saying that there exists a property $S$ called entropy such that a change in its value is equal to $S_2-S_1 = \int_1^2 dQ/T$ for any reversible process. In this case, thermodynamic systems, which are not explicitly mentioned but are implicitly understood to be items to which entropy is attributable, satisfy conditions (a), (b), and (c) with respect to the law. However, there are cases in which objects or substances not mentioned in a formulation might conceivably be taken to satisfy conditions (a), (b), and (c), and yet I should not want to classify them as a subject. For example, hydrogen gas might be said to satisfy these conditions with respect to the ideal-gas law 'All gases satisfy the relationship $pV = RT$', yet I should not want to say that hydrogen gas is a subject of this law. In such cases I adopt the procedure described in the third paragraph above and designate as a subject only the more general objects or substances. That is, if $S_1$ and $S_2$ could both reasonably be said to satisfy conditions (a), (b), and (c), and if being an $S_1$ logically entails being an $S_2$ but not conversely, and if there is no more general $S_3$ that also satisfies (a), (b), and (c), then $S_2$ can be designated as a subject but $S_1$ cannot.

It is not my claim that formulations of a law explicitly mentioning what can be classified as a subject, or even placing it as the grammatical subject, are always the most desirable ones. The desirability of a given formulation depends on what use is being made of the law in a given context. Nor am I saying that a regularity expressed by a law can be attributed to substances and objects only, and never to properties, states, events, or processes. I am simply suggesting certain categories that will be useful in the analysis that follows.

These categories may be rejected by those who say that laws are really about all items in the universe, and so if anything is to be treated as a subject of a law it can only be the latter type of thing. On this view, there is only one proper formulation of Gay-Lussac's law, viz.: 'All items in the universe are such that if they are gases then they combine with other gases in simple ratios by volume.' So formulated, it might be said, we can see that the subject must be items in the universe, the antecedent condition that of being a gas, and the consequent condition that of combining with other gases in simple ratios by volume.

Perhaps this formulation is equivalent to more standard formulations of Gay-Lussac's law, but this is not sufficient to establish that items in the universe are classifiable as a subject of Gay-Lussac's law, even in such a formulation. What must be shown is that such items satisfy conditions (a), (b), and (c) for being a subject of this law. Now while it is certainly true that items in the universe would be investigated in testing the law, it is not items, as such, that would be; i.e. items would not be chosen to test the law because they satisfy the description 'being an item in the universe', and this is what condition (b) is to be understood as requiring. Nor can 'combines with gases in simple ratios if a gas' be classified as a property or characteristic of items in the universe, as I have characterized these notions on pp. 19–20. (If we appeal to the fact that the description 'combines with gases in simple ratios if a gas' is true of a certain item then either we presuppose that the latter is an (actual) item in the universe or we do not. If we do not, if the item in question can be a hypothetical or imaginary one to which the above description can truly apply, then the fact that it satisfies this description would provide no basis at all for concluding that it is an item in the universe. In the former case the fact that an item in the universe satisfies the description would count in favour of such a conclusion not because the description is satisfied but only because we are assuming to begin with that what satisfies it is an item in the universe.) And if we say that 'combines with gases in simple ratios if a gas' is a regularity exhibited by all items in the universe, then we will be adopting a completely latitudinarian notion of regularity according to which anything whatsoever that can truly be said of any $X$'s describes a regularity that $X$'s exhibit, which would render this notion useless for characterizing scientific laws. Moreover, if something is a regularity (or, for that matter, a property or characteristic) exhibited by $X$'s, then it should also be a regularity exhibited by any particular $X$'s, i.e. by any items that satisfy the condition of being an $X$. So if we say that 'combines with gases in simple ratios if a gas' is a regularity (property, characteristic) exhibited by all items in the universe, we shall have to say that it is a regularity exhibited by items such as cows, neutrons, and automobiles, which seems absurd.[1]

Equally important is the fact that there is no reason for regarding the above formulation of Gay-Lussac's law as the only proper one, or as one that precludes the choice of gases as a subject. Even on this formulation gases are items a regularity in whose behaviour the law could be said to describe, that would be investigated in testing the law, and that could be said to have the property or characteristic of combining in simple ratios by volume.

A similar reply can be made to those who note that any statement of the form 'All *A* is *B*' is logically equivalent to 'All non-*B* is non-*A*', e.g. 'All gases combine in simple ratios by volume' is equivalent to 'All things that do not combine with each other in simple ratios by volume are not gases'. Such a formulation does not make non-*B*'s the only possible subject of the law, or a reasonable one. Items that do not combine in simple ratios by volume are not, as such, the type of items that would be investigated in testing Gay-Lussac's law, even in its present formulation. And to speak of not being a gas as a regularity exhibited by items that do not combine in simple ratios by volume (and so by cows etc.), or as a property or characteristic of such items, is to stretch the use of the terms 'regularity', 'property', and 'characteristic' beyond recognition.

I have spoken of laws of the form 'All *A* is *B*', but a few laws are customarily expressed in the negative form 'No *A* is *B*'. In such cases, instead of saying that all objects or substances of a certain sort exhibit a specifiable regularity, the law can be construed as saying that no objects or substances of a certain sort exhibit a specifiable regularity. The second law of thermodynamics, in the Kelvin formulation, says that no machine can exhibit the regularity of receiving heat continuously from a single source and converting this heat completely into work. The same law, in the Clausius formulation, says that heat cannot exhibit the regularity of passing spontaneously from a colder to a hotter body. In such cases subjects can be taken to be types of objects or substances that cannot exhibit the regularity described, machines in the first case and heat (if treated as a substance)[2] in the

---

[1] One reason we regard it as absurd is that we cannot appeal to the fact that something is a cow in explaining why if it is a gas it combines with gases in simple ratios. This relates to a point about laws to be discussed in chapter III, and I do not want to make this a defining condition for subjects of laws.

[2] If heat is treated as a state of a thermodynamic system, then thermodynamic systems can be taken to be a subject.

second. These are items that are investigated in testing the law. They are also items to which the non-existence of such regularities could reasonably be ascribed as properties or characteristics. It is a property of machines that they cannot receive heat continuously from a source and convert it completely into work, and of heat that it cannot pass spontaneously from one body to another at a higher temperature.

## 2. Criteria of Generality

We are now in a position to consider the question of generality. There is not one respect but several in which laws are general:

(1) Laws are syntactically general in the sense that they are formulated beginning with a universal term 'All' or 'No' followed by a subject term; or they can be so formulated, in a reasonable manner, without change of meaning, i.e. by means of a logically equivalent formulation. Laws say that all or no items of certain sorts exhibit certain regularities.

(2) Whatever can reasonably be called subjects of laws are general. They will be items like bodies (Newton's first law), thermodynamic systems (first law of thermodynamics), electrolytes (Faraday's first law), and gases (Gay-Lussac's law), rather than items like projectiles, mixtures of ice and water, copper sulphate solutions, or hydrogen. The generality of subjects in the case of laws is to be understood by contrast with the generality of subjects in propositions of other sorts. (In what follows I shall apply the categories of subject and of antecedent and consequent condition to propositions expressing regularities, whether or not they have sufficient generality to be called laws.) Two contrasts are important here: (a) A subject of a law is general by contrast with subjects of propositions describing the more particular regularities that the law can be used to analyse and explain. For example, what can reasonably be taken to be a subject of Newton's first law, bodies, is general by contrast with items such as projectiles and tops, which are subjects of regularities that Newton's law is used to analyse and explain. In such cases a subject $S'$ is more general than $S$ if all items that are $S$ are $S'$ but not conversely. (b) Within a given science or field a subject of a law is general by contrast with subjects of certain other propositions in that science or field. A science or field might be thought of as concerned with certain types of properties exhibited by substances or objects; thermodynamics with properties such as pressure, volume, temperature, energy, entropy, etc.; mechanics with position, velocity, momentum, force, energy, work, etc. Now

if there are laws within such a science or field then subjects of these laws will be substances or objects that can exhibit such properties, and they will be general by contrast with other sorts of subjects that can also exhibit such properties. Again, $S'$ can be regarded as more general than $S$ if all items that are $S$ are $S'$ but not conversely. The subjects of laws in thermodynamics will be thermodynamic systems rather than, say, mixtures of ice and water; subjects of laws in mechanics will be bodies or particles, rather than, say, projectiles or tops. To be sure, if what we count as a science or field is permitted to be as narrow as we please, then any items, no matter what their generality, are possible candidates for subjects of laws in some science or field. However, this is not entirely arbitrary, since the notions of science and field are not used in a completely unrestricted fashion. A physicist may study mixtures of ice and water, but there is no science of such mixtures, nor is this a field of physics.

The criterion of generality in (b) is the same as in (a), viz. class inclusion, but in (b) we relativize it to a science or field. This means that when we consider generality in a subject of a law we do so not simply by contrast with generality in subjects of propositions expressing regularities which the law explains and analyses, but also within a given science or field, by contrast with other items that can exhibit properties of concern to that science or field.

(3) To introduce a third aspect of generality, let me speak of a restricted universal. I shall say that a sentence is being used to express a restricted universal if it begins with a universal term, has a subject term, antecedent, and consequent conditions, and is being used to express a proposition a sufficient condition for whose truth is that each item that now actually satisfies the subject term and antecedent condition also satisfies the consequent condition (or fails to do so, if the universal term is 'No'). The sentence 'All men in this room are bald' would normally be used to express a proposition a sufficient condition for whose truth is that each man now in the room is bald. It is, then, normally used to express a restricted universal. We might speak of degrees of restriction. The sentence 'All men in this room are bald' might be used to express a proposition a sufficient condition for whose truth is that each man that now is or will ever actually be in this room is or will be bald when he is in the room. It would then be used to express a universal that is less restricted than the previous one. Laws express universals even less restricted than this. It is not a sufficient condition for the truth of Galileo's law that all bodies that

are actually unsupported now or even in the past or future fall with uniform acceleration. For Galileo's law to be true it is necessary that all bodies, at least all bodies much less massive than the earth, whether or not they are or ever will be unsupported, be such that if they were unsupported near the surface of the earth they would fall with uniform acceleration. It is not a sufficient condition for the truth of Snell's law that all rays of light that actually will strike a plane separating two media will be refracted in accordance with the formula sin $i$/sin $r$ = const. For Snell's law to be true it is necessary that any ray of light, whether or not it actually strikes a plane separating two media, be such that if it did strike such a plane it would be refracted in this manner. Those laws, then, that contain a subject term and antecedent and consequent conditions are general in the sense that they express unrestricted rather than restricted universals. They say something about all items satisfying the subject term and not just about those of these that do now, will later, or once did satisfy the antecedent condition.

(4) A law is general in the sense that what it says about a subject is supposed to hold for every particular sample or instance. What Boyle's law says about gases is supposed to apply to any sample of a gas; what Snell's law says about light rays is supposed to be true of each one. By contrast, the proposition (expressed by the sentence) 'All gases are studied by the chemist' does not say something about gases that is supposed to hold for every sample of gas; it is not general in an important respect. Rather it says something only about each type of gas. More precisely, we might distinguish propositions of the form 'All items satisfying a subject term $S$ satisfy a consequent condition $C$ (if they satisfy an antecedent condition $A$)', in which the (conditional) satisfaction of $C$ is being attributed to each individual item or sample that is an $S$, as well as to each type of $S$, from those propositions of this form in which the satisfaction of $C$ is being attributed only to types. Laws are propositions of the former sort. Here the question of the range of sizes of samples or instances to which a law applies might be raised. Boyle's law is not supposed to hold for a single gas molecule, and there is some question whether the second law of thermodynamics, in the entropy formulation, holds for the entire universe considered as an isolated thermodynamic system. The range in sizes of samples or instances to which a law is supposed to apply, and to which it in fact applies, are matters for the scientist to determine.

I have cited four respects in which laws are general, each of which can be appealed to in providing at least one reason why certain propositions are typically not classified as laws. 'The planet mars has a diameter of 4,230 miles' is not a law because, among other things, it lacks even the syntactic generality of one. It is not, nor can it reasonably be, formulated beginning with a universal term; thus it fails to satisfy condition (1). 'All cannon-balls, if unsupported, fall with uniform acceleration' is not a law, although it is formulated beginning with a universal term, since its subject is not sufficiently general by contrast with subjects of other propositions that can be used to explain and analyse the regularity expressed by this one, and by contrast with more general subjects in the field(s) of physics with which the present proposition is most naturally associated; thus it violates (2). The proposition that would normally be expressed by 'All solids in my room conduct electricity' does not satisfy condition (3) since, being a restricted universal, it does not say something about all solids but only about those now actually in my room. 'All gases are studied by the chemist' fails to satisfy condition (4) since it does not say something applicable to each sample of gas.

How are these four conditions related? In one way or another all of them are concerned with the generality of subjects of laws. Condition (1) indicates that laws ascribe a regularity to all items satisfying a subject term, and conditions (3) and (4) extend and clarify this idea, the former by indicating that a regularity is being ascribed to all such items and not just to those that do or will satisfy the antecedent condition, the latter by indicating that 'all items' covers instances or samples and not just types. Condition (2) imposes a restriction upon the generality of the subject term itself.

Are these respects the only ones in which laws are general? Are there, for example, generality criteria that apply to the antecedent and consequent conditions of a law? I shall approach these questions through a discussion of a traditional issue, viz. whether or not laws can mention specific objects, places, or times.

The proposition 'Any body if unsupported at the top of the Empire State Building will fall in accordance with the formula $s = \frac{1}{2}gt^2$' satisfies all the previous conditions. It is general in form, what can be classified as its subject, bodies, is general, it is not a restricted universal, and what it says about bodies is supposed to hold for every one; yet it is surely not a law. Why not? Some writers argue that laws are general in the sense that they do not mention specific objects, places, or times. The above proposition mentions the Empire State Building, a specific object, and so it is not general in an important respect. Yet some propositions actually classified as laws are not general in this sense. Kepler's laws mention a specific object, the sun, and Galileo's law, as well as the law of the simple pendulum, can be formulated so as to make explicit reference to a specific place, the vicinity of the earth. Moreover, suppose there were some body $B$ which repelled other bodies in its vicinity with a force varying as the inverse cube of the distance between them. If $B$ has a mass of $m_1$ and

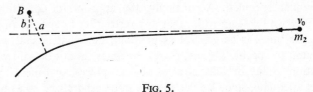

FIG. 5.

some other body repelled by $B$ has a mass of $m_2$ and the distance between the bodies is $r$, then the magnitude of the force of repulsion is $m_1 m_2/r^3$. At a very large distance from $B$ the body of mass $m_2$ is moving with a velocity $v_0$ in such a way that if it were not deflected by $B$ it would pass within a distance $b$ of $B$. However, it is deflected in such a way that its closest distance is $a$, as shown in Fig. 5. Using the first three laws of Newtonian mechanics, and in addition the proposition that the force varies as the inverse cube of the distance, the distance $a$ can be determined as a function of $b$, $m_1$, and $v_0$: $a = (b^2 + m_1/v_0^2)^{\frac{1}{2}}$. Suppose, on the basis of observations of the deflection of various bodies in the vicinity of $B$ in a way that satisfies the equation above, it is concluded that $B$ exerts an inverse-cube force on other bodies and furthermore that $B$ is the only body known to do so. Establishing this would be no simple matter, since it would have to be determined that there are no other bodies in the vicinity, that bodies are thus repelled whether or not they are electrically charged, small or large, made of one material or another, and so forth; it would also have to be determined that other bodies that have been observed are unlike $B$. However, if it were accepted that $B$ is the centre of a field of fixed force varying as the inverse cube of the distance, we might then speak of this as a gravitational law that governs that particular body, and the law might be formulated as follows, explicitly mentioning $B$: All bodies in the vicinity of $B$ are repelled by *B* with a force varying as the inverse cube of the distance from *B*.

What, then, is the difference between 'Any body if unsupported at the top of the Empire State Building will fall in accordance with the formula $s = \frac{1}{2}gt^2$', which we would hesitate to call a law, and our imaginary law formulated above? In the former case we need not have restricted what is said to the Empire State Building. We know that the same can be said for a body in any location near the surface of the earth. In the latter case the restriction to body *B* is essential. We are imagining that only body *B* causes other bodies to behave in the manner specified. Accordingly, the appropriate condition on generality would seem to be that any restriction to specific objects, places, or times is as general as possible; i.e. what is said with a restriction to specific objects, places, or times cannot be said with a restriction to any broader class of objects, places, or times. This is not yet adequate, since Kepler's laws can be generalized so as not to refer to the sun and the planets. They can be formulated so as to refer to the motion of any body under the action of a central inverse-square force, where the path of the body represents a curve whose eccentricity is greater than 0 and less than 1. Yet the laws were formulated by Kepler as laws about the motions of planets around the sun. Kepler did not know of this generalization, nor was the fact that his laws could be generalized obvious on the basis of the information available to him.

Accordingly, we might express the present condition epistemologically: For it to be reasonable at a given time to classify some proposition as a law it must be reasonable at that time, on the basis of the information available, to believe that any specific objects, places, or times mentioned are as general as possible, or at least it must not be obvious how they could be made more general. But this would make it unreasonable for us now to classify Kepler's propositions as laws. Evidently, if something was once classified as a law the label may stick even if later it was discovered how to make the law more general. What we could say, then, is the following:

(5)  For it to be reasonable at a given time to classify some proposition as a law it must be reasonable at that time, or it must have been reasonable at some previous time when it was classified as a law, to believe that what is said with a restriction to specific objects, places, or times cannot be said with a restriction to any broader class of objects, places, or times; or at least it must not be (have been)

obvious how such restrictions can be made more general. A restriction to a specific object, place, or time would be made more general by mentioning a type of item or condition that determines a class which contains the specific object, place, or time. In the example 'Any body if unsupported at the top of the Empire State Building will fall in accordance with the formula $s = \frac{1}{2}gt^2$' we could make the restriction to the Empire State Building more general by speaking of bodies satisfying the condition of being unsupported in any location near the surface of the earth.

According to (5) it is still reasonable to classify Kepler's propositions as laws, since there was a time when they were so classified when it was not obvious how they could be generalized. Moreover, by appeal to this condition it is possible to settle the dispute between those who affirm and those who deny that laws can mention specific objects, places, or times. The physicist Maxwell held the latter view, although he stated it with reference to Newtonian mechanics: 'The difference between one event and another does not depend on the mere differences of the times or the places at which they occur, but only on differences in the nature, configuration, or motion of the bodies concerned.'[1] Put more generally, it might be said that laws describe conditions under which events occur that are independent of the times and places at which they occur. Moritz Schlick, taking an opposing view, argued that it would be possible for a law to mention specific places and times:

Now again I certainly expect that all laws of nature will actually conform to Maxwell's criterion . . .—none the less it remains theoretically possible that a future physics might have to introduce formulae which contain space and time in an explicit form, so that the same cause would never have the same effect, but the effect would also depend, in a definite way, e.g., on the date, and would be different tomorrow, or next month, or next year.[2]

Schlick goes on to say that the important thing is predictability. If a proposition enables the prediction of future events then it can be a law whether or not it mentions specific places or times.

Condition (5) settles this dispute by admitting that there is a sense in which both disputants are right. It is reasonable to classify as a law a proposition mentioning specific objects, places, or times, but only if it is also reasonable to believe, or to have believed, that what is said

[1] J. C. Maxwell, *Matter and Motion* (New York, 1920), p. 13.
[2] M. Schlick, 'Causality in Everyday Life and in Recent Science', reprinted in *Readings in Philosophical Analysis*, ed. H. Feigl and W. Sellars (New York, 1949), pp. 528–9.

of these cannot be said of a broader class of items that possibly can be characterized without mention of specific objects, places, or times. Can we, then, accept this condition as supplying a criterion of generality for laws? Not as it is, I believe, because it is a special case of an even more general condition. What we require is not simply that what is said with a restriction to specific objects, places, or times cannot be known or believed to be attributable to a broader class of items, but that what is said of a subject satisfying any antecedent condition, whether or not reference is made to specific items, cannot be known or believed to be attributable either to a more general subject, or to a subject satisfying a more general antecedent condition, or to both. For example, if it is and was always reasonable to believe that solids generally and not just solid pieces of copper expand when heated in a way that satisfies the equation $L_t = L_0(1+at)$, where $L_t$ is length at temperature $t$ and $a$ is a constant for each solid, then this proposition if restricted only to solid copper would not be classified as a law. Moreover, we require that what is said about a subject cannot be known or believed to be capable of being said in a more general way about that subject or about a more general type of subject.

Let me make this more precise by introducing some definitions. First, how can we compare two subjects, two antecedent conditions, as well as two consequent conditions with respect to generality? I shall employ a criterion used earlier and say that subject $S'$ is more general than subject $S$ if the following is true: Anything that is $S$ is $S'$ but not everything that is $S'$ is $S$. The truth may be empirical or analytic. I shall say that antecedent condition $A'$ is more general than $A$ if the following is an empirical or analytic truth: Any $S$ that satisfies $A$ satisfies $A'$ but not every $S$ that satisfies $A'$ satisfies $A$. And I shall say that consequent condition $C'$ is more general than $C$ if the following is an empirical or analytic truth: Any $S$ that satisfies $C$ satisfies $C'$ but not every $S$ that satisfies $C'$ satisfies $C$. (In what follows, to avoid trivialization a subject term more general than $S$ will not be permitted to be constructed simply by taking $S$ in alternation with some other arbitrarily chosen term; similarly for the antecedent and consequent conditions.) On this definition 'solid' designates a subject more general than 'solid copper', 'being heated' is a more general antecedent condition than 'being subjected to a gas flame', and 'expanding in accordance with the formula $L_t = L_0(1+at)$' is a more general consequent condition than 'expanding in accordance with the formula $L_t = L_0(1+16\cdot7\times10^{-6}t)$'.

Suppose that $L$ and $L'$ are two propositions that are not logically equivalent and that begin with a universal term and contain a subject term, (possibly) an antecedent condition, and a consequent condition. With respect to a given choice of subject terms and antecedent and consequent conditions, I shall say that $L'$ is a generalization of $L$ if (a) $L'$, together possibly with other propositions that are true, entails $L$, but these other propositions do not themselves entail $L$, and (b) the subject term of $L'$ is more general (in the sense defined above) than the subject term of $L$, or the antecedent condition of $L'$ is more general than the antecedent condition of $L$, or the consequent condition of $L'$ is more general than the consequent condition of $L$, or all or any of these obtain. For example,

(i) All solids when heated expand in accordance with the formula $L_t = L_0(1+at)$

is a generalization of

(ii) All solid copper when subjected to a gas flame expands in accordance with the formula $L_t = L_0(1+16\cdot7\times10^{-6}t)$

with respect to the choice of 'solid' as the subject term of (i), 'being heated' as an antecedent condition, and 'expanding etc.' as the consequent condition, and with respect to the choice of 'solid copper' as the subject term of (ii), 'being subjected to a gas flame' as an antecedent condition, and 'expanding etc.' as the consequent condition. This is so because 'solid' is more general, in the sense previously defined, than 'solid copper'; 'being heated' is more general than 'being subjected to a gas flame'; 'expanding in accordance with the formula $L_t = L_0(1+at)$' is more general than 'expanding in accordance with the formula $L_t = L_0(1+16\cdot7\times10^{-6}t)$'; and proposition (i), together with the true propositions that something subjected to a gas flame is heated, and that $a$ (the coefficient of linear expansion) for copper is $16\cdot7\times10^{-6}$, entails proposition (ii). We can then say that $L'$ is a generalization of $L$ if there are reasonable choices of subject terms and antecedent and consequent conditions for $L$ and $L'$ with respect to which $L'$ is a generalization of $L$.

It is now possible to replace (5) with the following criterion of generality:

(5)′ If it is reasonable at time $t$ to classify $L$ as a law then either:

(a) there is not known at $t$ any proposition $L'$ which is known or believed to be a generalization of $L$ in any of its equivalent formulations and which is believed is or might be true; or

**(b)** at some previous time $t^*$ when $L$ was known and was classified as a law there was not known any proposition $L'$ of the sort described in (a).

According to this condition it would not be reasonable to classify proposition (ii) as a law if it is reasonable to suppose that those acquainted with (ii) would also be capable of thinking of its obvious generalization (i), which they would believe is or might be true. In short, it is not reasonable to classify something as a law if a generalization of it is known that is believed is or might be true. However, if such a generalization of a proposition $L$ is now known but was not at some previous time when $L$ was classified as a law it may still be reasonable to classify $L$ as a law, according to (5)′. Kepler's laws are still reasonably called laws, even though generalizations of them are believed to be true, since there was a time when they were classified as laws when such generalizations were not known.

Condition (5)′ includes the phrase '$L$ in any of its equivalent formulations'. This is meant to cover empirically equivalent as well as logically equivalent formulations.[1] On my definitions, $L'$ might be a generalization of $L$ in one of its equivalent formulations but not another. Condition (5)′ requires that no generalization of any equivalent formulation of $L$ is believed to be true. Note also that (5)′ does not necessarily preclude classifying as laws propositions that when known were always known to be entailed by other laws or theories. For example, even if Newton's laws of motion had been known as long as the law of conservation of momentum, and even if it had always been known that the former entail the latter, this would not prevent the latter from being classified as a law. What is required in order to reject a 'law' classification is that the entailing law or theory be known or believed to be a generalization of the given proposition, and the conjunction of Newton's laws was not known or believed to be a generalization, in my sense, of the law of conservation of momentum.

Condition (5)′ is relevant for the classification of those propositions making reference to specific objects, places, or times. It is possible to classify such propositions as laws provided that any propositions known or believed to be generalizations of them are not believed to be true, or provided that any such generalizations were not believed to be true at some time in the past when they were classified as laws. Kepler's laws, which mention a specific object, satisfy this condition

---

[1] See chapter I, section 3.

in virtue of satisfying the second part of it. Earlier we considered an imaginary inverse cube law which satisfies this condition in virtue of satisfying the first part. We also considered the proposition 'Any body if unsupported at the top of the Empire State Building will fall in accordance with the formula $s = \frac{1}{2}gt^2$ '. This is not a law, since it fails to satisfy either part of condition (5)'.

Finally, we might contrast condition (5)' with the previous four conditions. Condition (5)' is different from the others since, for one thing, it is stated epistemologically, whereas the others are not. For another, it is broader, since it is concerned with generality not just in subjects but in antecedent and consequent conditions as well. We might wonder whether in the light of (5)' we really need (2), which imposes generality on subject terms. Since (5)' requires that the subject term of a law be believed to be as general as possible, it might be said that (2) ought to be construed as a special case of (5)' or as a first approximation to it. I am not convinced of this. Note, to begin with, that (2), strictly speaking, is not a special case of (5)', since the latter but not the former states an epistemological condition. That (2) ought to be thought of as a first approximation to (5)' and should thereby be discarded in favour of it is not obvious. We tend to reject the classification 'law' for proposition (ii) above, not only because it violates (5)' but also because it violates (2), i.e. because its subject term, 'solid copper', is not sufficiently general within physics or chemistry or within fields of these sciences. Even if we did not know of any generalization of (ii) which we believed is or might be true we would hesitate to classify (ii) as a law, because of lack of generality in its subject term; or at least this would count to some extent against a law classification. If we lived in a world in which regularities could only be attributed to items of very narrowly defined types my claim is that there would be some hesitancy in speaking of such regularities as laws. However, I do see a tension between (2) and (5)'. The fact that a subject term of a proposition is not very general within a given science or field may make us hesitate to classify the proposition as a law. The fact that it is the most general subject to which that regularity, or a generalization of it, is believed to be attributable may incline us in the opposite direction.

## 3. Other Views of Generality

It might be useful to compare the criteria of generality I have formulated with those cited by other philosophers of science. Hempel and

Oppenheim distinguish fundamental laws from propositions which are logically derivable from them, which they call derivative laws, and they propose the following criteria for generality in fundamental laws:[1] A law is general in the sense that (a) it begins with a universal term, and (b) none of its terms makes explicit reference to any one particular object or space-time location. This is certainly not sufficient to characterize the generality of the sorts of propositions I am classifying as laws. For example, these criteria are satisfied by 'All copper melts at 1,083 °C', whose subject term lacks sufficient generality to allow the proposition to be called a law. Moreover, although condition (a) is one I would accept, condition (b) is not. As already indicated, there are propositions actually classified as laws, and others that might well be, containing terms making explicit reference to a particular object or space-time location.

In a later work Hempel substitutes for (b) the following requirement: (c) A law 'must not be logically equivalent to a finite conjunction of singular sentences'.[2] By a singular sentence Hempel means a sentence with a syntactic form such as $Pa$, in which a predicate $P$ is attributed to a particular item designated by $a$. But unless further requirements are made concerning what is to count as a singular sentence, laws such as those of Kepler, Galileo, and the imaginary inverse-cube law, the first two of which, at least, Hempel is willing to classify as laws, can all be formulated as singular sentences. For example, in Kepler's first law, $a$ could be the sun, and $P$ the predicate 'is at one focus of an ellipse that is the path taken by planets'. Hempel recognizes this problem, but claims that it can be solved by expressing statements in a suitably formalized language that contains quantificational notation and in which each extra-logical term is either primitive or definable by reference to primitive terms.[3] A sentence of such a language can then be called singular if it is logically equivalent to a sentence containing no defined terms and no quantifiers. This proposal, however, is of no avail until it is embellished with principles for deciding which terms to treat as primitive. For example, if the predicate 'is at one focus of an ellipse that is the path taken by planets' is treated as primitive—and Hempel offers no reason why it could not be—then Kepler's first law can be stated as a singular

[1] C. G. Hempel and P. Oppenheim, 'The Logic of Explanation', reprinted in *Readings in the Philosophy of Science*, ed. H. Feigl and M. Brodbeck (New York, 1953), pp. 319–52.

[2] Hempel, *Aspects of Scientific Explanation* (New York, 1965), p. 340. See also p. 292.    [3] Ibid., p. 356.

sentence, and hence it could not be a law, according to Hempel's criterion.

Ernest Nagel, in his discussion of laws, espouses condition (a), a condition very much akin to (c), and in addition a condition that can be expressed like this: The class of items examined as evidence for the law must not be known to be identical with the class of those that actually do satisfy a subject term and antecedent condition of the law; or, as Nagel puts it, 'the evidence for the law must not be known to coincide with its scope of predication'.[1] Moreover, he adds, 'its scope is not known to be closed to any further augmentation'.[2] Nagel's requirement is too strong, for suppose Kepler had examined data regarding the paths of all nine planets and had known there are and will be only nine. Nagel's condition would then preclude classifying Kepler's propositions as laws. Or suppose there were a unique volume of space in which objects obeyed a different force law, and suppose further that there were just two bodies in that volume and that it is known to be virtually impossible for these bodies to escape or for others to enter. We might still speak of the force law obeyed by bodies satisfying the antecedent condition of being in that volume, even though Nagel's requirement is not met, i.e. even though the class of items examined as evidence coincides with the 'scope of predication' of the law and this scope is known to be closed to augmentation.

Hans Reichenbach proposes several generality criteria for what he calls 'original nomological statements', including (a) above and a rough equivalent of (b).[3] He also suggests two additional criteria. One, to complement (a), would preclude propositions like 'All unsupported bodies fall with uniform acceleration and gases exist', which contain as separable parts statements that are not 'all-statements'.[4] The other criterion, which complements (b), is quite complex, but its main consequence can be stated as follows, using terminology of the previous sections: Suppose it is a fact that whatever satisfies a subject

[1] E. Nagel, *The Structure of Science* (New York, 1961), p. 63.

[2] It is clear that Nagel is referring to the class of all those items that actually do or will satisfy a subject term and antecedent condition, and not to any class of items satisfying a subject term that, in some sense, could but will not actually satisfy the antecedent condition. See Nagel, op. cit., p. 63.

[3] H. Reichenbach, *Elements of Symbolic Logic* (New York, 1947); *Nomological Statements and Admissible Operations* (Amsterdam, 1954). For illuminating discussions see E. K. Jobe, 'Some Recent Work on the Problem of Law', *Philosophy of Science*, 34 (1967), 363–81; H. A. Lauter, 'An Examination of Reichenbach on Laws', *Philosophy of Science*, 37 (1970), 131–45.

[4] *Nomological Statements and Admissible Operations*, p. 30.

term, or antecedent condition, or both, of a certain proposition exists within a given, restricted space-time region ('such a region might be given by part of the earth's surface during a certain time, or by a galaxy'); and suppose this fact can be verified as true; then the proposition lacks sufficient generality to be a law.[1] This seems to have the effect of ruling out Galileo's law if the antecedent condition is construed as 'being unsupported in the vicinity of the earth', and if we can assume that the earth will exist for a finite length of time. For similar reasons it appears to preclude the imaginary inverse cube law described earlier.

Of the criteria for generality cited in section 2, only the first, syntactic generality, is included in the views of Hempel, Nagel, and Reichenbach. The only other generality criterion these authors mention which is related to ones I have proposed is that laws include reference to no specific objects, places, or times, or that they not be equivalent to singular sentences. The first alternative is too restrictive, the second possibly as well, unless vagueness is removed from the notion of a 'singular sentence'. In any case this condition is really a special case of a more general one, viz. (5)', that has to do not only with what the law mentions but also with our knowledge concerning the law and any of its generalizations. The remaining conditions (2)–(4) that I formulated are nowhere discussed by these authors, since they seem to be concerned with a much broader concept of law. However, these conditions are relevant, I believe, in determining those aspects of generality in virtue of which some propositions are and others are not classifiable as laws in science.

[1] Ibid., pp. 36–8. Quotation from p. 38.

# III. The Necessity of Laws

## 1. Some Standard Views

The concept of necessity has intrigued philosophers from Aristotle to twentieth-century Positivists. In dealing with it various contrasts, such as that between necessity and contingency, necessity and possibility, and necessity and accident, are usually drawn. In recent philosophy of science the latter contrast has been the one of concern in the case of laws. Laws are held to express that which must be, that which occurs of necessity, and they are contrasted with what are called 'accidental' generalizations such as 'All men in this room are bald'. Sentences of the latter sort, it is claimed, do not say what must be; they do not express necessity. What is meant by 'necessity' here, what is the basis for this contrast, and what features do laws possess in virtue of which necessity might be attributed to them?

One widespread view is that to say of a sentence that it is necessary is to say that it is or is deducible from a law, something that cannot be said of an 'accidental' generalization.[1] Such a view is not helpful if we want to attribute necessity to laws themselves and to explain what this means. Another view is that to attribute necessity to a law is to say that it is the sort of statement in universal form that can 'serve as a basis for an explanation', whereas 'accidental' generalizations cannot.[2] Such a view is also unhelpful, at least if stated in this simple way. Here is a perfectly good explanation for which it seems appropriate to say that an 'accidental' generalization serves as a basis: The reason that all men in this room are wearing hats is because all men in this room are bald, and it is very cold in this room.

Another view is that laws but not 'accidental' generalizations are well supported by the evidence. Such a basis for the contrast, like its predecessors, is spurious. The 'accidental' generalization 'All men in

---

[1] See H. Reichenbach, *Elements of Symbolic Logic*, and *Nomological Statements and Admissible Operations*.

[2] C. G. Hempel, *Philosophy of Natural Science* (Englewood Cliffs, N.J., 1966), p. 56.

this room are bald' might be well supported by the evidence: we might have observed all men in the room, under ideal conditions of observation, and found each one to be bald. Sometimes it is said that laws are different from 'accidental' generalizations in that positive instances tend to add confirming weight to laws but not to 'accidental' generalizations.[1] For example, the fact that a certain unsupported body falls with uniform acceleration adds confirming weight to the law that all unsupported bodies do. By contrast, the fact that a certain man in the room is bald adds no confirming weight to the generalization that all men in the room are bald. Such a claim, I think, is based on an incorrect account of confirmation. If we generalize from the behaviour of one unsupported body but not from the baldness of one man we do so because we possess additional information about bodies and men. Whether positive instances tend to confirm a proposition depends not only on the proposition but on what else is known. For example, if we know that two organizations are convening in separate rooms in a certain hotel, one a Bald Man's organization the other a Hairy Man's, then the fact that one man in this room has been observed to be bald would add confirming weight to the assertion that all men in this room are bald.

Another claim is that a law, unlike an 'accidental' generalization, supports a counterfactual. For example, Galileo's law supports the counterfactual 'If this (supported) body were unsupported it would fall with uniform acceleration', whereas 'All men in this room are bald' does not support the counterfactual 'If this (hairy) man were in the room he would be bald'. I find this claim somewhat hazy. What is meant by saying that a law *supports* a counterfactual? Does it mean that the law implies the counterfactual, or simply that the counterfactual can be defended by appeal to the law, even though there need be no implication, or something else? What sort of counterfactual is in question? Clearly some would have to be disallowed. 'All men in this room are bald' might be taken to imply, and be used to defend, the counterfactual 'If you were identical with one of the men in this room you would be bald'. Shall we take the counterfactual to be a general one of the form 'Anything is such that if it were . . .', or a specific one of the form 'If such and such an item were . . .'? If general, shall we take it to be saying that anything that satisfies a subject term is such that if it were to satisfy an antecedent condition then it would satisfy the consequent condition ('Any body is such

[1] N. Goodman, *Fact, Fiction, and Forecast* (Cambridge, Mass., 1955), p. 74.

that if it were unsupported it would fall with uniform acceleration')? Or shall we take it to be saying that anything is such that if it were to satisfy a subject term and an antecedent condition it would satisfy the consequent condition ('Anything is such that if it were a body that is unsupported it would fall with uniform acceleration')?

Most important, when we employ a counterfactual we often do so making certain assumptions regarding what other conditions, in addition to the counterfactual one, are to change or stay the same. Let's return to our Bald Man's convention and suppose that all men in this room are bald. Under one set of assumptions, viz. that Jones would be a member of the Bald Man's organization and not necessarily retain the present number of hairs on his head, we could say: 'If Jones were in this room he would be bald.' Under another set of assumptions, viz. that he would retain the present number of hairs on his head and would not be a member of this organization, we could not say this. Whether 'All men in this room are bald' can be thought of as supporting the present counterfactual depends on what further assumptions are made, and these can vary with the situation in which the counterfactual assertion is made.

It might be replied that in the case of laws there is at least this difference. Whereas in some contexts an 'accidental' generalization can be thought of as supporting a given counterfactual and in others not, in all contexts a law can be thought of as supporting a counterfactual, no matter what assumptions are made in those contexts. This I would deny, for the same problem can arise with laws and counterfactuals. Can the law 'All ideal gases satisfy the relationship $pV = RT$' be thought of as supporting the counterfactual 'If the substance in that jar, which happens to be lead, were an ideal gas it would satisfy the relationship $pV = RT$'? It depends upon what assumption is made. One is that the substance in that jar comes to have the properties of an ideal gas. Another is that the substance in that jar remains lead but the label 'ideal gas' comes to be used in such a way that it is applicable to it. Under the first assumption the ideal-gas law could be thought of as supporting the counterfactual in question, under the second assumption it could not. Either assumption might be made when this particular counterfactual is asserted.

Finally, the categories of necessity and accident are not exhaustive, as the above views seem to suggest. It may be no accident that all men in this room are bald, since there is a Bald Man's organization meeting here. But, in an important sense, it is not necessary either, for Jones, who is hairy, could easily wander into the room by mistake, or the organization could have met elsewhere. Nor is it clear, even, that attributions of necessity and accident are mutually exclusive. It may be regarded as a coincidence that all of the men in this room are bald, since it may be a coincidence that these particular men are in this room. But it may also be regarded as necessary that all of the men in this room are bald, since all of them have the gene for baldness.

## 2.  Criteria for the Non-accidental and for the Necessary Character of Laws

Having criticized several attempts to characterize that in virtue of which necessity is attributed to laws, can something positive be said? I believe there is not one feature of laws but several which may be involved in the attribution of necessity to them, and these have not been sufficiently sorted out and characterized. More precisely, these are features in virtue of which laws can be said to express either what is necessary, or what is non-accidental or non-coincidental,[1] or both. Some of these features are suggested in views I have rejected, but none has been stated in a way that is free from difficulties. In my discussion I shall again employ the concepts of subject and antecedent and consequent condition. If more than one item can reasonably be classified as a subject of a given law and more than one condition as an antecedent or consequent condition, then what is said is meant to hold for all that can. In what follows I shall continue to use the term 'law' in the propositional sense. However, some of the features I mention can be ascribed to such propositions only if there are facts which they (correctly) express, i.e. only if there are laws in the 'fact' sense. In such cases I shall speak of a proposition as *expressing* a law.

(1) If a proposition expresses a law then the fact that an item satisfies a subject term and antecedent condition (if any) can be appealed to as offering a correct explanation, or at least a part of such an explanation, of why it satisfies the consequent condition. Coulomb's law says that two particles oppositely charged with electricity will attract each other in accordance with the formula

$$F = q_1 q_2/r^2.$$

The fact that two items are particles oppositely charged with electricity can be cited in correctly explaining why they are attracting

---

[1] In what follows I use the terms 'non-accidental' and 'non-coincidental' interchangeably, although they are by no means synonymous.

each other in accordance with this formula. Explanation is a subject I will treat in chapter IV. For the moment, suffice it to say that one correctly explains why these two items are attracting each other in this manner if one provides a correct answer to the question 'Why are these two items attracting each other in this manner?' As I shall emphasize later, what can count as a correct answer to a given question depends, in part, on standards of correctness that are appropriate for the situation in which the question is raised. So, according to the present condition, the fact that an item satisfies a subject term and antecedent condition can be appealed to as providing what, in a given situation, can be regarded as a correct answer, or at least a part of such an answer, to the question 'Why does it satisfy the consequent condition?'

It might be objected that some laws violate this condition. For example, the Wiedemann–Franz law states that the ratio of thermal conductivity $K$ to electrical conductivity $s$ is a constant

$$L \left( = \tfrac{1}{3}\pi^2(k/e)^2 \right)$$

for all metals. But the fact that the electrical conductivity of a metal is such and such cannot be regarded as correctly explained in any situation by saying that its thermal conductivity is such and such. This objection loses its force if we note that in accordance with our previous definition, neither thermal conductivity nor electrical conductivity can be designated as subjects of the law, since neither are substances or objects. If we take metals as a subject and construe 'have a ratio of thermal to electrical conductivity $= L$' as a consequent condition, then, indeed, why some item has a ratio of thermal to electrical conductivity $= L$ can be correctly explained by appeal to the fact that it is a metal. Even if we take metals as a subject and construe 'has a thermal conductivity of $K$' as an antecedent condition and 'has an electrical conductivity of $s = K/L$' as consequent condition, it is by no means precluded that why an item has an electrical conductivity of $s = K/L$ can be correctly explained, at least in part, by appealing to the fact that the item is a metal and that it has a thermal conductivity of $K$.

The present feature is one in virtue of which propositions that express laws can be said to express what is non-accidental or non-coincidental. By contrast, suppose that within a given situation the claim is made that it is accidental, or a coincidence, that all men in this room are bald. One thing that might be meant is this: the fact that someone is a man who is in this room cannot be appealed to as offering what in that situation can be regarded as a correct explanation, or a part of a correct explanation, of why he is bald; his being bald cannot be appealed to as offering such an explanation of why he is a man who is in this room; nor are there facts that can be appealed to in providing such an explanation of his being a man who is both in this room and bald. His being bald and his being a man in this room, as we might say, have nothing to do with each other. More generally, within a given situation the proposition 'All $S$'s that satisfy condition $A$ satisfy condition $C$' can be regarded as expressing what is accidental or coincidental, in the present sense, if the following conditions are satisfied: (a) the fact that something is an $S$ that satisfies $A$ cannot be appealed to as providing what, in that situation, can be regarded as a correct explanation, or a part of such an explanation, of why it satisfies $C$; (b) the fact that something satisfies $C$ cannot be appealed to as providing such an explanation of why it is an $S$ that satisfies $A$; (c) no facts can be appealed to as providing such an explanation of why something is an $S$ that satisfies both $A$ and $C$. I emphasize that this is just one sense in which the proposition 'All $S$'s that satisfy $A$ satisfy $C$' might be said to express what is coincidental or accidental. In another sense, as we shall see later, the very same proposition might be said to express what is non-coincidental. In the present sense, laws do not express what is accidental or coincidental because they fail to satisfy condition (a).

But, it will be objected, what about the Bald Man's convention? In this case the fact that a man is bald can be appealed to as offering a correct explanation, or at least a central part of such an explanation, of why he is in this room. I agree, but if there is an organization of bald men meeting here then it can be regarded as no accident or coincidence that all men in this room are bald. One difficulty with the positions I have been criticizing is that they concern themselves with sentences only. According to such positions the sentence 'All men in this room are bald' is an accidental generalization. What I have said should make it evident that it is not sentences that are accidental, in the present sense, nor is it propositions. Just by examining the sentence 'All men in this room are bald', or the proposition it expresses, it is impossible to determine that it is an accident or coincidence that all men in this room are bald. What is accidental or a coincidence, or better, what can be so regarded, is the fact that the proposition is true.

If a sentence in universal form is used in a certain situation to express a proposition the truth of which can be regarded as an accident or coincidence, in the present sense, I shall say that the sentence, as used in that situation, expresses an *accidental universal*. The sentence 'All men in this room are bald' may or may not be used in such a way that it expresses an accidental universal. If it does not, this will not make the proposition it expresses a law, since, for one thing, it lacks sufficient generality. For another, the fact that it is not a coincidence that a proposition is true does not make it necessary that it is true.

In the previous chapter I spoke about *restricted universals*. A sentence is being used to express a restricted universal if it begins with a universal term, has a subject term, antecedent and consequent conditions, and is being used to express a proposition a sufficient condition for whose truth is that each item that now actually satisfies the subject term and antecedent condition also satisfies the consequent condition. The sentence 'All men in this room are bald' would normally be used to express a proposition a sufficient condition for whose truth is that each man now actually in this room is bald. It would, then, normally be used to express a restricted universal. As used, it may or may not express an accidental universal.

Philosophers have not sufficiently distinguished these two types of universals, which they often classify together simply as 'non-lawlike'. Moreover, the restricted universal is not sufficiently distinguished from another type which might seem to be restricted, although it is not, or at least not in the same sense. Consider Galileo's law expressed with the following qualification: 'Any body much smaller than the earth that is unsupported near the surface of the earth will fall toward the earth with uniform acceleration.' In one sense, to be sure, this law is restricted. Uniform acceleration is being attributed to bodies *much smaller than the earth* only if they are unsupported in the *vicinity of the earth*. However, the law is not restricted in the sense previously defined, since it is not a sufficient condition of its truth that each small body that is now actually unsupported in the vicinity of the earth is falling with uniform acceleration. For it to be true it is necessary that any small body, whether or not it actually is, was, or ever will be unsupported near the surface, falls in this manner if unsupported.

I have cited one feature of laws in virtue of which they can be said to express what is non-accidental or non-coincidental. It is not a feature sufficient to warrant the attribution of necessity. The mere fact that it is not a coincidence, in the present sense, that a certain proposition is true does not warrant the inference that what it says holds necessarily or with necessity or that the fact that it expresses is a necessary one.

(2) Necessity can be ascribed to a law—we might say that the law must be true, that what it says must hold—if there are facts that provide strong support in its favour and against its competitors. Necessity, in the present sense, can of course be attributed to any sort of proposition, whether or not it is a law. We can say of a proposition that it must be true since other propositions are true, and what we mean is that the latter propositions strongly support the former and undermine its contraries.

However, there is this difference between laws and many other propositions, including accidental universals, for which strong support can exist. Because of their nature and the nature of their support, propositions classified as laws are treated as propositions that are not to be readily abandoned. By this I mean that if someone purports to have discovered that there is something satisfying a subject term and antecedent condition but not the consequent condition there is a strong tendency to refrain from rejecting the law, or at least from rejecting it completely, and instead to do one of three things:

(a) Say that the subject term and antecedent condition are not really satisfied. For example, the law of conservation of energy, as applied to the phenomenon of beta decay, requires that the energy available for a nuclear disintegration be constant. If so then all beta particles emitted should have the same energy, but in fact they have quite different energies. Instead of admitting that this falsifies the law physicists suggested that a subject term and antecedent condition of the law were not really satisfied, since not all particles in beta decay had been taken into account. The existence of the neutrino was postulated, in addition to the recoil nucleus and beta particle, as carrying off some of the energy.

(b) Say that the law is restricted in its application to certain kinds of cases. The restriction might be made explicitly in the formulation of the law by adding qualifications to an antecedent condition or it might be understood implicitly. The law of Dulong and Petit states that the product of the atomic weight of a solid element and its specific heat is a constant, whose value is 6·3. Indeed, Dulong and Petit originally formulated the law to cover all elements, not just solid ones. ('The atoms of all simple bodies have exactly the same capacity for heat.') It was found that the lighter solid elements deviate considerably from this value, but instead of rejecting the law scientists considered its application restricted to the heavier solid elements.

(c) Say that the law is an approximation. The Rayleigh–Jeans law states that any black body emitting radiation of wavelength $\lambda$ does so in such a way that the intensity of radiation $\psi_\lambda$ satisfies the relationship $\psi_\lambda = 8\pi k T \lambda^{-4}$, where $T$ is the absolute temperature of the enclosure through which radiation is emitted and $k$ is Boltzmann's constant. At short wavelengths, however, this was found to disagree considerably with observation, and a law developed later by Planck was accepted. In Planck's law the formula is

$$\psi_\lambda = \frac{8\pi ch}{\lambda^5} \frac{1}{e^{ch/\lambda kT} - 1}.$$

Nevertheless, the Rayleigh–Jeans law is retained for certain purposes, and is treated as a useful approximation for longer wavelengths.

In cases (b) and (c) it is admitted that strictly speaking the law, as presently formulated, is false. Nevertheless, it can be modified by introducing restrictions which render it correct, or it can be utilized to give results that are approximately correct, or both. In such cases the evidence obtained can be said to support the claim that the law holds in a restricted domain or that it is approximately true.[1]

Is there support for laws generally? A proposition may be classifiable as a law even if there is no fact which it expresses, but if it was once thought to express a fact of a certain sort. A law, in this sense, may be false, though its defenders will have believed that there is evidence in its favour. In most such cases the evidence its proponents believed was efficacious can be construed as supporting the claim that the law holds in a restricted domain or that it is approximately true. A proposition is not ordinarily classified as a law until strong evidence is marshalled in its favour, which may later turn out to support only a limited version of the law.

The motivation to retain propositions that are or come to be classified as laws can be explained by appeal to the kind of propositions that laws are as well as to the type of support in their favour. In chapter I, I said that laws are treated as revealing in a precise way the regularities that underlie other regularities, and in chapter II that they are general in many respects. Accordingly, they provide explanations

---

[1] Cf. M. Scriven, 'The Key Property of Physical Laws—Inaccuracy'. For a discussion of procedure (a) above see E. Nagel, *The Structure of Science*, pp. 64 ff.

and analyses that are relatively fundamental and precise, and do so for broad classes of phenomena. The discovery of such explanations and analyses is one of the central aims of the scientist, so he is strongly motivated to search for laws and to retain them once found, though allowing for the possibility of modification. Moreover, the fact that a given law is capable of furnishing fundamental and precise explanations and analyses for broad classes of phenomena can provide support for it.[1] Indeed, laws typically receive support from varied sources and not simply, and sometimes not even at all, from finding items satisfying a subject term and antecedent condition which also satisfy the consequent condition. This may be because of the difficulty of observing items satisfying a subject term and an antecedent condition or determining whether the consequent condition is satisfied—owing to the fundamental, abstract, and quantitative character of the law. It may also be because of the difficulty of observing a large number and variety of instances—owing to the law's generality. Therefore, support often comes not just from instances or from these together with the types of explanations and analyses the law can provide. It may also come from theories. Maxwell derived his distribution law for molecular velocities from theoretical assumptions of kinetic theory. Support may come from analogies with other known facts. Priestley suggested the plausibility of an inverse-square law for electric charges by analogy with Newton's inverse-square law of gravitation.[2] Because of the varied character of support frequently enjoyed by a law, its rejection may require major changes elsewhere; e.g. changes in a theory which provides a basis for the law or in others that may utilize it, rejecting explanations provided by the law of possibly many and diverse data. Accordingly, there is usually considerable motivation for retaining a law, and, in the face of seeming counter-instances, for saying either that a subject term and antecedent condition are not really satisfied, or that the law is restricted to certain cases, or for treating the law as a useful approximation.

Compare laws with universals that are both accidental and restricted, the sort of universal that can be expressed by the sentence 'All men in this room are bald'. Such universals may be strongly supported by the evidence, but they do not express regularities as basic as those expressed by laws, nor with the same amount of completeness and precision. Accordingly, they are not capable of explaining regularities in as general, complete, or precise a manner as laws;

[1] See chapter VI.    [2] See chapter VII.

hence there is not a comparable sort of motivation for retaining them. Typically, their support comes solely from 'nose-counting'—from observing items satisfying a subject term and antecedent condition that also satisfy the consequent condition. And their rejection would not require major changes elsewhere in hypotheses and explanations that are accepted. Both laws and accidental universals may have strong support, but the support enjoyed by a law, unlike an accidental universal, is often of a systematic sort that makes abandoning it much more difficult and unlikely.

(3) To describe a third feature of laws, one in virtue of which they can be said to express what is necessary, I shall invoke the idea of 'supporting counterfactuals' discussed earlier, but now try to state it more carefully. Problems arose earlier because it was not clear what counterfactual is in question, how it is related to the law, and what assumptions are allowable when the counterfactual is asserted. To proceed I shall employ a useful way of presenting the situation introduced by Nicholas Rescher.[1]

Rescher points out that when we make a counterfactual assertion we do so in the context of a certain set of beliefs that we hold. We then make an assumption which is logically incompatible with the conjunction of these beliefs, requiring one or more of them to be abandoned. Which we abandon will determine what counterfactual we assert, but logic alone cannot dictate which to abandon. For example, we believe that all bodies that are unsupported fall with uniform acceleration. We may also believe that some particular body is supported at time $t$ and that it is not falling with uniform acceleration at $t$. Suppose now we make the (counterfactual) assumption that this body is unsupported at $t$. Rescher's way of representing this is as follows:

Beliefs:    (1) All bodies that are unsupported fall with uniform acceleration.
            (2) Body $B$ is supported at time $t$.
            (3) Body $B$ is not falling with uniform acceleration at $t$.

Assume: Body $B$ is unsupported at time $t$.

Under this assumption we must abandon (2), but then we cannot retain both (1) and (3). Abandoning (3) and retaining (1) is tantamount to accepting the counterfactual 'If body $B$ were unsupported

[1] N. Rescher, 'Belief-contravening Suppositions', *Philosophical Review*, 70 (1961), 176–96; see also *Hypothetical Reasoning* (Amsterdam, 1964).

at time *t* it would fall with uniform acceleration at time *t'*. Abandoning (1) and retaining (3) is tantamount to rejecting this counterfactual. Which move we make is not dictated by consideration of logical consistency, but, says Rescher, if (1) is a law, then this decides the matter, for laws are to be retained above non-laws. Such a decision, indeed, is required by a feature of laws we have just finished noting, viz. that they are treated as propositions not to be readily abandoned.

Compare this case with an analogous one involving the proposition 'All men in this room are bald'.

Beliefs:    (1) All men in this room are bald.
            (2) Jones is a man not in this room.
            (3) Jones is not bald.

Assume: Jones is a man in this room.

Under this assumption we are to abandon (2), but we have a choice of abandoning (1) or (3). Since (1) is not a law we cannot use this reason for retaining it. So far, then, we have no basis for asserting (or denying) the counterfactual 'If Jones were in this room he would be bald'. However, as I indicated earlier, when a counterfactual is asserted or denied often additional assumptions are made regarding other conditions that are to change or remain the same. In the above case we may assume not only that Jones is a man in the room but also that he retains the present number of hairs on his head. This additional assumption requires us to keep (3) and abandon (1), and thus reject the counterfactual 'If Jones were in this room he would be bald'.

The case of the Bald Man's convention yields a different result. Here we have not only additional assumptions but additional beliefs.

Beliefs:    (1) All men in this room are bald.
            (2) All men in this room are here because they are members of organization *O*.
            (3) *O* is a Bald Man's organization, i.e. a necessary condition for membership is baldness.
            (4) Jones is a man not in this room.
            (5) Jones is not bald.
            (6) Jones is not a member of *O*.

Assume:    (a) Jones is in this room.
            (b) If Jones is in this room he is so for the same reason that everyone else is.
            (c) (2) and (3) above are to be retained.

On these assumptions, which require that we abandon (4), (5), and (6), we can make the following counterfactual assertion: 'If Jones were in this room he would be bald.'

Let me return now to laws. Suppose a term $S$ is reasonably designated as a subject term of a law, a condition $A$ as an antecedent condition, and a condition $C$ as a consequent condition. The first question we must answer is what sort of counterfactual laws are supposed to support. Consider some item $i$ that satisfies the subject term $S$ but not the antecedent condition $A$. The counterfactual in question is this: If $i$, which is an $S$, were to satisfy $A$ it would satisfy $C$. (I do not claim that this type of counterfactual is the only one supported by a law, only that it is one, and a central one.) Now with regard to such counterfactuals, laws are different from propositions like 'All men in this room are bald' in two respects. First, a law of the form 'All $S$'s that satisfy $A$ satisfy $C$' supports the counterfactual 'If $i$, which is an $S$, were to satisfy $A$ it would satisfy $C$' *without the need for any further assumptions* (i.e. beyond that $i$ is an $S$ which does not satisfy $A$). Second, this support is semantical entailment in the following sense: the meaning of the law is such that given a law of the form in question and given the fact that $i$, which is an $S$, does not satisfy $A$, it follows that if $i$ were to satisfy $A$ it would satisfy $C$. Earlier I indicated that laws are not restricted universals. It is not a sufficient condition for their truth that each $S$ that now satisfies the antecedent condition also satisfies the consequent condition. It is necessary that any $S$, whether or not it does or ever will satisfy the antecedent condition, be such that if it did it would also satisfy the consequent condition. This is part of what the law is asserting. Using Rescher's scheme we have the following type of situation:

Beliefs:   (1) All $S$'s that satisfy $A$ satisfy $C$.
             (2) $i$, which is an $S$, does not satisfy $A$.
             (3) $i$, which is an $S$, does not satisfy $C$.

Assume: $i$, which is an $S$, satisfies $A$.

If (1) is construed as a law then on the assumption that $i$, which is an $S$, satisfies $A$ we would retain (1), abandon (3), and assert the counterfactual 'If $i$, which is an $S$, were to satisfy $A$ it would satisfy $C$'. My claim is that if (1) is construed as a law then this counterfactual is entailed by (1) together with (2).

Consider now the non-law 'All men in this room are bald', where this is used to describe a situation that is entirely coincidental (in the sense given on p. 44), or else a situation that is not entirely coincidental (e.g. the Bald Man's convention). In the first case the proposition 'All men in this room are bald' would not be used to support the counterfactual 'If Jones were in the room he would be bald'. In the second case it could be, but only if additional beliefs are introduced and assumptions made regarding the Bald Man's convention. Moreover, it is not true that the proposition expressed by 'All men in this room are bald' together with the proposition 'Jones is a man not in the room' *entails* the counterfactual 'If Jones were in the room he would be bald'. Using Rescher's general scheme above, in such cases either we would not assert the counterfactual 'If $i$, which is an $S$, were to satisfy $A$ it would satisfy $C$' on the basis of (1) and (2), or if we could it would not be entailed by (1) and (2) alone but only if additional assumptions were introduced.

It should now be clear why the present formulation avoids pitfalls of the idea of 'supporting counterfactuals' noted in section 1. First, by requiring that the item cited in the counterfactual satisfy the subject term of the law we rule out cases such as the one in which it is to be assumed that lead is an ideal gas. The present requirement assures us that the item imagined can, in a reasonable sense, satisfy the antecedent condition. Second, by requiring that the counterfactual be supported without the introduction of further assumptions, beyond that $i$ is an $S$ and does not satisfy $A$, we preclude certain kinds of implicit assumptions that earlier caused embarrassment. In the baldness case we preclude the assumption that Jones, who is not now in the room, is a member of the Bald Man's organization. In the example in section 1, 'All men in this room are bald' could be taken to support 'If Jones were in this room he would be bald' because we made the assumptions that there is a Bald Man's organization meeting in this room and that Jones is a member of this organization. If we do not make these assumptions, or others like them, we are not entitled to assert that if Jones were in the room he would be bald. Third, by requiring that the counterfactual be entailed we remove ambiguity from 'supporting counterfactuals' and also exclude accidental and not-so-accidental universals.

Some laws involve no condition that could reasonably be designated as an antecedent condition. What can we say about these? In some cases inferences in certain respects analogous to those already treated can be made. Take Newton's law of gravitation, that any two bodies attract each other with a force proportional to the inverse square of the distance between them. In this case we can suppose that two bodies are closer together or farther apart than they now are. The law together with the proposition that these bodies are a distance $d$ apart implies that if they were a distance $d'$ apart (rather than $d$) then they would attract each other with a force proportional to the inverse square of $d'$ (rather than $d$). With other laws that lack an antecedent condition the inference may involve a counterfactual assumption to the effect that there is an additional item satisfying the subject term. Kepler's first law can be taken to imply that if there were an additional planet it would revolve about the sun in an elliptical orbit with the sun at one focus of the ellipse.

The present feature of laws, that there is a semantical entailment between a law, a statement about a particular item, and a counterfactual of a certain type, is one in virtue of which laws can be said to express what is necessary. The fact that 'All unsupported bodies fall with uniform acceleration' is to be understood in such a way, that together with 'This body is supported' it implies 'If this body were unsupported it would fall with uniform acceleration', means that it is to be understood as expressing a necessary relationship between being an unsupported body and falling with uniform acceleration. Galileo's law can be understood as saying that if some body is unsupported then it must fall with uniform acceleration, that being such a body makes falling in this manner necessary. By contrast, if the claim is made that the proposition 'All men in this room are bald' does not express something that is necessary, what may be meant is that such a proposition is not to be construed as expressing a necessary relationship between being a man in this room and being bald. It is not to be construed as implying that men, even if they are not now in fact in this room, would be bald if they were in this room.

The present feature of laws is also one in virtue of which they can be said to express what is non-accidental or non-coincidental. If 'All unsupported bodies fall with uniform acceleration' is to be understood in such a way that together with 'This body is supported' it implies 'If this body were unsupported it would fall with uniform acceleration', then the former proposition expresses a non-accidental or non-coincidental relationship between being an unsupported body and falling with uniform acceleration. We might say that it is no accident or coincidence that this unsupported body is falling with uniform acceleration, and our claim might be based on the assumption that any body, if it were unsupported, would fall in this manner.

(4) With some laws, though certainly not most, the necessary character attributed to them may derive from the fact that they are treated as expressing analytic truths. (If they are so treated they can also be said to express what is non-accidental or non-coincidental.) Someone is using a sentence to express an analytic truth if he is using it to express a proposition that he would defend, and properly so, solely by appeal to the use of terms in that sentence.[1] One type of analytic truth that can be expressed by sentences of the form 'All $X$'s are $P$' is that in which $P$ is logically necessary for being an $X$. There are some laws treated in this way. For example, the ideal-gas law, as often formulated, states that for an ideal gas the temperature, volume, and pressure are related according to the formula $pV = RT$. But as the term 'ideal gas' is used, satisfying this formula is a logically necessary condition for being an ideal gas. In accordance with this use, the law is being treated as expressing an analytic truth, indeed as a definition of the term 'ideal gas'. There is still an empirical issue, but it is not whether the law is true. It is whether any actual gases are ideal gases, or how closely actual gases approximate to being ideal gases.

There is another type of analytic truth that can be expressed by sentences of the form 'All $X$'s are $P$'. In this case $P$ is semantically relevant for $X$ without being logically necessary.[2] Briefly, to say that $P$ is semantically relevant for $X$ is to say that it is one among a set of properties in virtue of which items are classifiable as $X$'s, though some $X$'s, either actual or hypothetical, may lack some properties in this set. Lack of $P$ counts in and of itself to some extent against classifying an item as $X$, though it may not be decisive. Possession of $P$, given that the item possesses certain other properties, counts in and of itself to some extent in favour of classifying the item as $X$. For example, as many physicists and chemists use the term 'copper', having a melting point of 1,083 °C., is semantically relevant though not logically necessary for copper. This property is one among a set of properties in virtue of which items are classifiable as copper, though some $X$'s may lack some properties in this set. A substance might have all the properties of copper, except that it melts at 500 °C., and it might still be classifiable as copper, as the term is currently used.

Sentences ascribing a semantically relevant property of $X$ to $X$ can be used to express analytic truths. They can be used to express propo-

---

[1] See my *Concepts of Science*, chapter 1.     [2] See ibid., pp. 10–19.

sitions defensible solely by appeal to the use of the term '*X*'. For example, the sentence 'Copper melts at 1,083 °C.' can be used to express a proposition that could properly be defended by appeal to the fact that as the term 'copper' is used by scientists, items, both actual and hypothetical, are correctly classifiable as copper if and only if they have many or most of a certain set of properties among which melting at 1,083 °C. is semantically relevant. However, the sentence can also be used to express a different proposition, an empirical one, that could be defended by pointing out that substances with all the other properties of copper melt at 1,083 °C.

Some laws can be construed as ascribing semantically relevant properties of *X* to *X*. Newton's first law of motion states that bodies subject to no external forces will remain at rest or move in a straight line with uniform velocity. As the expression 'bodies subject to no external forces' is used by physicists, it is a semantically relevant property of such bodies that they remain at rest or move in a straight line with uniform velocity. This is one of several criteria in virtue of which bodies are classified as being subject to no external forces. Accordingly, Newton's first law can be construed, and sometimes is, as expressing an analytic truth, as ascribing a semantically relevant property of *X*'s to *X*'s. However, it can also be construed as expressing an empirical proposition that can be defended by pointing out that bodies subject to no external forces—as determined by criteria other than the one just cited—remain at rest or move in a straight line with uniform velocity.

(5) A law might be said to express what is non-accidental or non-coincidental if there is an explanation of why the law holds that can be regarded as correct. Consider Boyle's law. We might say that it is no accident that the pressure of a gas and its volume are related by the formula $pV = $ constant, when temperature is constant. We might say this because gases are composed of molecules having certain properties that can be appealed to in correctly explaining why gases obey Boyle's law. This might be said to be a perfectly reasonable sense of 'expressing what is non-accidental'. Notice, however, that it is one that holds as well for what I have been calling accidental universals (and, if we accept determinism, for all true propositions). For example, in this sense the accidental universal expressed by 'All men in this room are bald' expresses what is non-accidental. For one way of explaining why all men in this room are bald is by saying of each man in the room why he is bald, and surely for each man there

is some correct explanation of why he is bald. We should say, then, that there is a sense in which it can be regarded as accidental or a coincidence that all men in this room are bald, viz. the sense given in criterion (1) above. There is also a sense in which it can be regarded as non-accidental, viz. the sense in which there is a correct explanation of why each particular man in this room is bald; it is no accident, we might say, that all these men are bald.

Various qualifications might be added to the type of explanation in question, thereby changing to some extent the present sense of expressing what is non-accidental. We might say that a proposition expresses what is non-accidental if there is some correct explanation of why it is true which itself involves at least some propositions expressing what is non-accidental in one or more of the respects described in this section. Again, however, this would not exclude accidental universals. For example, it might be that all men in this room have a certain type of gene, and that according to genetic theory anyone with that gene is bald. To preclude such cases we must require that everything involved in a correct explanation be non-accidental or necessary in one or more of the respects previously discussed. An even stronger requirement would be that all propositions involved in the explanation satisfy criteria (2) and (3), i.e. that they be propositions for which there is strong support and that together with certain particular statements they entail counterfactuals of certain sorts. Another requirement might be that the propositions in the explanation entail, or otherwise provide strong support for, the proposition whose truth is being explained.[1] In the latter case, since there is strong support for the proposition, in accordance with the criterion discussed in (2) it is possible to attribute necessity to that proposition, and not merely the characteristic of expressing what is non-accidental. Indeed, I believe that there are laws and explanations for them that do satisfy this requirement. Necessity can be attributed to Boyle's law in virtue of the fact that why it holds (to the extent it does) can be correctly explained by employing kinetic theory whose assumptions entail the law in question.

If, as some might claim, there are correct explanations for all laws, then all laws can be regarded as expressing what is non-accidental in the present sense. If, as others might claim, not all laws can be

---

[1] According to a standard theory of explanation this requirement must be satisfied by all correct explanations. This theory is one I do not accept; it will be examined in chapter V.

explained—some are 'fundamental'—then the characteristic of expressing what is non-accidental, in the present sense, cannot be attributed to all laws. I do not propose to enter into this dispute, since I am not sure how it could be settled.

## 3. Conclusions

I have cited five features of laws in virtue of which they might be said to express what is necessary, what is non-accidental, or both. The characteristic of expressing what is non-accidental may be attributed to a law in virtue of the sort of relationship between subject term and antecedent and consequent conditions that the law is asserting, which allows certain types of explanations. Necessity may be attributed to a law in virtue of strong support in its favour. The characteristic of expressing what is non-accidental as well as what is necessary may be attributed to a law in virtue of the fact that together with a statement about a particular item it entails certain types of counterfactuals; in virtue of the fact that the law expresses an analytic truth; or in virtue of the fact that there is a correct explanation for the law (involving propositions of certain types). The first feature is shared by all propositions that express laws (facts); the third is shared by all propositions classifiable as laws, whether or not they express facts; the second is shared by most propositions classifiable as laws, provided that we allow the strong support to include support for the claim that the law holds in a restricted domain, or that it is approximately true, or both; the fourth is shared by some; the fifth is shared by some or all, depending on what sort of determinism is true and on what sorts of propositions are in the explanation.

Let me concentrate now on the features of necessity and relate these to a traditional distinction between absolute and relative necessity. It is held that necessity can be attributed to some propositions solely in virtue of the fact that other propositions are true. Such propositions are necessary relative to these other propositions; they are said to express what must be true, what is necessarily true, given that other propositions are true. Absolute necessity is attributed to propositions 'absolutely' and not in virtue of the fact that other propositions are true (or else in virtue of this fact provided that these other propositions are necessary in an absolute sense). Perhaps the clearest examples of propositions with absolute necessity are those that are analytic, and of propositions with relative necessity are those that are entailed by, or otherwise strongly supported by, true propositions that are not necessary in the absolute sense. In the latter case a proposition is necessary relative to the true propositions that entail it.

Of the features of laws noted in this chapter only (4), analyticity, seems to be a case of absolute necessity. (2) and one of the criteria discussed in (5) are cases of relative necessity. The fact that a proposition $p$ is strongly supported by a true proposition $q$, or the fact that $p$ can be correctly explained by being derived from a true proposition $q$ which either entails it or strongly supports it, makes it possible to say that $p$ must be the case since $q$ is. The counterfactual feature of laws described in (3) does not make laws necessary in an absolute or a relative sense. It does not enable us to say that a law must be true or that it is necessarily true. Nevertheless, this feature does warrant the claim that laws *express* what is necessary, and this claim is best viewed in connection with relative necessity. If a proposition $p$ is necessary relative to a proposition $q$ then some third proposition which expresses this fact can be said to express a necessary relationship between $p$ and $q$ or between the states of affairs described in $p$ and $q$. Consider a proposition of the form 'All $S$'s that satisfy $A$ satisfy $C$'. If this is construed as supporting counterfactuals in the sense previously indicated, and if the proposition is true, then we can say that if something is an $S$ that satisfies $A$ then it must satisfy $C$, or that being an $S$ that satisfies $A$ makes satisfying $C$ necessary. For example, if 'All unsupported bodies fall with uniform acceleration' is construed as supporting counterfactuals of the required sort, and if it is true, then if something is a body that is unsupported it must fall with uniform acceleration, being such a body makes falling in this manner necessary. If the proposition 'All $S$'s that satisfy $A$ satisfy $C$' supports counterfactuals in the appropriate sense then it can be construed as expressing a necessary relationship between being an $S$ that satisfies $A$ and satisfying $C$. By contrast, if the proposition 'All men in this room are bald' is construed as not supporting counterfactuals in the appropriate sense, then such a proposition does not express a necessary relationship between being a man in this room and being bald; being a man in this room does not make being bald necessary.

In sum, then, the necessity we attribute to a law may derive from three sources:

from the fact that it has strong support—feature (2), which explains why one of the features described in (5) permits the attribution of necessity;

from the fact that it supports counterfactuals of certain types—feature (3);

from the fact that it is analytic (if it is)—feature (4).

In virtue of features (2) and (4) we can say that a given law is necessarily true or that it must be the case; in virtue of (3) we can say that it expresses what is necessary, or more fully, that it expresses a necessary relationship.

On the basis of (2), (3), and (4) it is possible to understand why the feature of laws described in (1) does not by itself warrant the attribution of necessity to laws. Given a proposition of the form 'All $S$'s that satisfy $A$ satisfy $C$', the fact that it is possible to appeal to something's being an $S$ that satisfies $A$ in correctly explaining why it satisfies $C$ does not by itself guarantee that such a proposition satisfies either (2), (3), or (4). This fact does not guarantee that there is strong support in favour of the proposition, or that it is analytic. That this fact fails to guarantee that the proposition supports counterfactuals, in the appropriate sense, can be made clear by considering the following proposition: 'All of the men who are the President's advisers are in room $A$.' It may be possible to correctly explain why some particular person is in room $A$ by appeal to the fact that he is one of the President's advisers, but we need not construe the proposition in such a way that, together with 'Jones is a man who is not one of the President's advisers', it entails 'If Jones were one of the President's advisers he would be in room $A$'.

On the basis of (2), (3), and (4) it is also possible to understand why the main feature described in (5) does not warrant the attribution of necessity to laws. The fact that there is an explanation of why a proposition is true that can be regarded as correct does not by itself guarantee that the proposition satisfies (2), (3), or (4). This fact does not guarantee that the proposition supports counterfactuals of certain types, and it does not make it analytic. Nor does this fact by itself guarantee that the proposition has strong support. The fact that I have explained why $p$ is true by appeal to $q$, and that this explanation can be regarded as correct, does not necessarily mean that $q$ provides strong support for $p$. Some correct explanations do, whereas some do not, provide such support for the propositions they explain.[1]

General conclusions can now be drawn that have a bearing on some traditional claims about laws, necessity, and accident.

(a) Of the features of laws discussed in the previous section that pertain to necessity and accident, two are semantical and three are not. That a law, together with certain other propositions, entails counterfactuals of certain sorts, and that it is analytic (if it is), are

[1] See chapter V.

semantical facts about the proposition that is or expresses the law, in a way in which the fact that an item's satisfying a subject term and antecedent condition of a law can be appealed to in providing a correct explanation of why it satisfies the consequent condition, the fact that there is strong support for the law, and the fact that there is a certain type of explanation of why the law holds, are not. The former but not the latter are characteristics that can be determined solely by considering the proposition in question. Accordingly, I reject the view which says that the question of whether a sentence expresses what is accidental or what is necessary is a semantical one that can always be answered simply by considering the proposition which that sentence is supposed to express. I also reject the view according to which if a proposition is held to express what is necessary it cannot also be held to express what is accidental or coincidental. From one point of view we may regard the fact that the proposition 'All men in this room are bald' is true as a coincidence—there is no explanatory connection between being bald and being in this room. From another point of view we may regard it as necessary—all the men in this room have the gene for baldness.

(b) The features I have mentioned in virtue of which necessity, as well as the characteristic of expressing what is non-accidental, can be attributed to laws are not features peculiar to laws. There are many non-laws to which each of them can be attributed. Accordingly, citing these features does not suffice to pick out the class of laws, though of course some, viz. (1) and (3), can be regarded as characteristics of all propositions that express laws, and others as characteristics of some. There is a view according to which necessity is peculiar to laws, and indeed should be defined in terms of the concept of law. To say that a proposition is necessary, on this view, is to say that it is a law or that it is deducible from one. This position I find unappealing. For one thing it fails to provide a necessary condition for necessity, since propositions can be regarded as relatively necessary if they are entailed by true propositions that are not laws, and as absolutely necessary if they are analytic without being, or being deducible from, laws. For another thing, although this view does supply a sufficient condition for necessity, this fact is not very illuminating, since the view fails to answer the question of why a proposition that is a law is necessary. What features do laws possess in virtue of which it is possible to attribute necessity to them? My task in the present chapter has been to answer this question.

# IV. Explanation

Laws play important roles in explanations in science. One type of explanation has already been noted, viz. explaining why something satisfies the consequent condition of a law by appeal to the fact that it satisfies a subject term and an antecedent condition. But just how is this explanatory, and in what other ways do laws function in explanations? To answer these questions we must provide an analysis of the general concept of explanation. This is the aim of the present chapter. In chapter V the ideas to be developed here will be applied to the case of laws.

Philosophers who write about explanation usually distinguish what they call its 'logical' aspects from its 'pragmatic' ones. Having done so they concentrate solely on the former, and as a result tend to create a one-sided and, I believe, inaccurate picture. I shall propose an analysis that, I think, has some advantages over such accounts. It covers a larger group of explanations; it spells out the contextual nature of explanation; it cites criteria for evaluating explanations and indicates how the applicability of these criteria depends on the situations in which explanations are offered. Since my analysis appeals to the concept of understanding, I plan to say something about this as well.

## 1. 'Explain'

In one sense, everyone would agree that the authors of the Bible explain the origin of man; in another sense, many would disagree. The former sense might be paraphrased by saying that the authors of the Bible attempt to explain, the latter by saying that they correctly or satisfactorily explain. In the first three sections I shall be concerned with the former sense, and so will use the expression 'attempt to explain'. My question is this. What does it mean to say that someone would attempt to explain something $q$ by citing something $E$?

What someone would cite in attempting to explain $q$ depends in part on the sort of person to whom he is explaining. How I would attempt to explain the rainbow, Boyle's law, or the concept of entropy to children in the third grade will differ in important ways from how I would do this in a college physics course. Furthermore, when I attempt to explain $q$ I may cite several things or just one. If several, one of them may be the most central, and I may be willing to call it my explanation of $q$. I shall refer to what is cited as $E$, where this may be one thing or several. We have, then, the following schema:

I. *A* would attempt to explain *q* to those in situation *S* by citing *E*, or by citing a number of things of which *E* is the most central.

What can be substituted for the various schematic letters? For $A$ (the explainer), persons and groups of persons. For $E$ (what is cited in explaining), one or several events, facts, phenomena, states of affairs, propositions (including things such as laws, theories, and books, which are, or are composed of, propositions). For $S$ (the situation), information about the knowledge and particular concerns (questions, puzzles, unclarities) of persons to whom $A$ is attempting to explain $q$. For $q$ (the explained), many things, e.g. a — (fact, state of affairs, event, phenomenon, concept, proposition, theory, book, poem, etc.), the — of — (structure of the atom, meaning of this poem), as well as many sorts of questions in *oratio obliqua* form, e.g. why — (that happened), how — (a steam engine works), what — (occurred, the difference is between a baryon and a lepton), how possibly — (that could have occurred), and so forth. It will simplify the presentation if we can suppose that any $q$ that is explained is, or is transformed into, a question or set of questions in *oratio obliqua* form. Instead of '*A* would attempt to explain this phenomenon' we can say '*A* would attempt to explain how (or why) this phenomenon occurs' or '*A* would attempt to explain what the nature of this phenomenon is'. In what follows, $Q$ will be used to designate a question and $q$ the *oratio obliqua* form of that question.

Invoking the concept of understanding, schema I can, I suggest, be expressed as follows:

II. *A* would attempt to render *q* understandable to those in situation *S* by citing *E*, or a number of things of which *E* is the most central, as providing what *A* believes is or might be a correct answer to *Q*.

I shall defer until later an analysis of understanding. Several preliminary points must be made regarding schema II.

(1) Often people attempt to explain things by providing what they

believe to be a correct answer. But sometimes their attempt is made in the spirit of exploration. If a physicist is in the midst of developing a nuclear theory, he might attempt to explain why certain nuclear phenomena occur by providing not what he definitely believes is a correct answer but what he believes might be correct. Still, it may be asked, can't $A$ attempt to explain $q$ to those in $S$ by deliberately providing what he believes to be an incorrect answer to $Q$? In schemas I and II my concern is only with sincere, honest, genuine, attempts to explain. If someone deliberately provides what he believes to be an incorrect answer to $Q$ I shall not count this as an attempt to explain.

(2) I am using 'understandable' in such a way that if $q$ is understandable to those in $S$ then those in $S$ actually understand $q$. So we can also say that if $A$ is attempting to explain $q$ to those in $S$ by citing $E$ then he is attempting to make those in $S$ understand $q$ by citing $E$ as providing what he believes is or might be a correct answer to $Q$. The fact that someone is not attempting to render $q$ understandable to those in $S$ in such a way counts decisively against saying that he is attempting to explain $q$ to them, and the fact that he is attempting to render $q$ understandable to those in $S$ in this way counts decisively in favour of saying that he is attempting to explain $q$ to them.

This might be denied. It might be claimed that $A$ could cite $E$ in order to render $q$ understandable to those in $S$ without necessarily attempting to explain $q$ to them. Suppose I know that the statement 'God is love' is so causally efficacious with you that the mere uttering of it will cause you to understand anything, and in particular why atoms emit only discrete radiation. If so, I might say 'God is love' thereby attempting to make you understand why atoms emit only discrete radiation, even though by saying that I would be making no attempt to explain anything to you. But this in no way shows that schema II inadequately expresses schema I, for I do not believe that 'God is love' does or might provide a correct answer to the question 'Why do atoms emit only discrete radiation?' and this is required by schema II. Not every way of attempting to render $q$ understandable counts as attempting to explain $q$.

The converse might also be rejected. It might be denied that attempting to explain $q$ to those in $S$ requires attempting to render $q$ understandable to those in $S$. Suppose a physicist introduces the concept of entropy to students in a third-grade class and proceeds in the same way he does in his college thermodynamics class, knowing full well that the third graders will not be able to understand what he is saying, and not attempting to make them understand this. Isn't he, nevertheless, attempting to explain to them what the concept of entropy means? He is attempting to cite to those in $S$ what he believes is a correct answer to $Q$, and this may make us want to say that he is attempting to explain $q$ to those in $S$. But then we must add that he is treating those in situation $S$ as if they were in situation $S'$; he is attempting to explain $q$ to those in $S$ under the supposition that they are not in $S$. So we might also say, with appropriate emphasis, that he is not really attempting to explain $q$ *to those in S*. Either way, we cannot say, at least not without qualification, that our physicist is attempting to explain $q$ to those in $S$. What necessitates the qualification is precisely the fact that he is not attempting to render $q$ understandable to those in $S$.

(3) Usually if $A$ is attempting to explain $q$ to those in $S$ then it is implicit that those in $S$ do not already understand it. But sometimes they do, and $A$ may know this. $A$ may attempt to explain the concept of entropy to his teachers who already understand it perfectly well. However, if he does this then there is a sense in which he is treating them as if they did not understand this concept. Accordingly, in schema II, when I speak of attempting to render $q$ understandable to those in situation $S$, I mean to those who do not, or (in the appropriate sense) can be treated as if they do not, understand $q$.

(4) To attempt to explain $q$ to those in $S$ one need not attempt to render $q$ understandable in all respects, i.e. so that no further questions could be raised concerning it. Rendering $q$ understandable to those in $S$ involves providing an answer to $Q$, which in turn may involve providing an answer to other questions that might be raised in $S$ by those who do not understand $q$. It does not involve providing an answer to every question that might be raised by anyone at all who does not understand $q$. What questions need to be answered will vary with the knowledge and concerns of those in $S$ and with the sort of explanation the explainer thinks appropriate under the circumstances (more about this in section 4).

(5) I have spoken about attempting to explain. What about successfully explaining? If we say that $A$ successfully explained $q$ to those in $S$ by citing $E$, this would mean that $A$ succeeded in rendering $q$ understandable to those in $S$ by citing $E$ as providing what $A$ believes is or might be a correct answer to $Q$; i.e. by citing $E$ as providing such an answer, $A$ succeeded in getting those in $S$ to understand $q$.

(6) In recent years philosophers have spoken about illocutionary

acts such as stating, describing, promising, raising a question, and asserting, which are performed by uttering certain words with certain intentions. The notion was introduced originally by Austin,[1] and has been developed more recently by Searle,[2] who has described categories of rules or conditions for performing such acts. Explaining, in the sense under discussion, i.e. attempting to explain by citing something, is an illocutionary act, and it might be useful to relate what I have said so far to Searle's discussion. Searle divides rules governing illocutionary acts into four types: propositional-content rules, which concern the type of proposition that is involved in the performance of the act, preparatory rules, which concern the sort of position (regarding knowledge, beliefs, capabilities) the utterer should be in to perform the act, sincerity rules, which concern the utterer's sincerity, seriousness, honesty, in performing the act, and essential rules, which concern the point of the act. To relate this to my analysis of attempting to explain, we might isolate various elements of that analysis that are governed by such rules. For example, we might say that $A$ attempts to explain $q$ to those in $S$ only if the following rules or conditions are satisfied: $A$ cites something $E$ that is or can be described in a proposition (propositional-content rule); $A$ believes that the citing of $E$ will provide what is or might be a correct answer to $Q$ and that those in $S$ do not understand $q$ or can be treated as if they do not (preparatory rule); $A$ is attempting to provide what he believes is or might be a correct answer to $Q$ (sincerity rule); $A$'s citing of $E$ counts as an attempt to render $q$ understandable to those in $S$ by providing a correct answer to $Q$ (essential rule).

## 2. Explanation

Can schema I, understood in the sense of schema II, be used to define 'explanation'? To begin with, 'explanation' has an act-content ambiguity. In referring to $A$'s explanation we may be referring either to his act of explaining or to what explains, according to $A$. In the former sense we can speak of $A$'s explanation as something that took so much time, while in the latter sense we cannot, because we are referring not to the act of explaining but to what was cited in the performance of this act. I am concerned with the latter sense. 'Explanation' has a second ambiguity. If I describe something as

---

[1] J. L. Austin, *How to Do Things with Words* (Oxford, 1962).
[2] J. Searle, *Speech Acts* (Cambridge, 1969).

being an explanation of *q*, I may mean that it is a good or satisfactory explanation, or my description may carry no such implication. I am concerned with the latter sense of 'explanation', the sense in which bad as well as good explanations are classifiable as explanations.

Schema I contains the formula '*A* would attempt to explain *q* to those in situation *S* by citing *E*'. The variable '*E*' ranges over such things as events, facts, phenomena, states of affairs, and propositions. These are items that are cited when someone attempts to explain something. These are also items that can be said to be or to provide explanations. We may say of a mine cave-in (an event), or of the fact that the mine caved in, or of the weakened condition of the walls of the mine that led to the cave-in (a state of affairs), or of the proposition expressed by the sentence 'the mine caved in', that it is or provides an explanation of what caused the death of the miners. If we say that an *E is* an explanation of *q*, we are using the 'is' of classification, not identity. So the formula we want to consider is this: '*E* is classifiable as being or providing an explanation of *q*.' How shall this formula be defined? Appealing to schema I, we might be tempted to propose the following definition:

*E* is classifiable as being or providing an explanation of *q* if and only if there is some *A* and some situation *S* such that schema I is satisfied, i.e. such that *A* would attempt to explain *q* to those in *S* by citing *E*, or by citing a number of things of which *E* is the most central.

There are difficulties with this calling for a contextual relativization in the definition. If 'there is some *A*' means 'there now exists some *A*' then the definition precludes explanations that would have been given by past *A*'s, or explanations that would have been given by no actual *A* in the past, present, or future, but by imagined *A*'s. Suppose we ask: How many explanations of the distribution of galaxies are there? Shall we say two—the steady state and the big bang? Shall we include those offered in the past but completely rejected today? Can we count one my nine-year-old son invented, or one that hypothetical persons might have offered? There is no answer independent of the context in which such questions are raised. Whether *E* is classifiable as an explanation depends in part on the context of classification *C* in which what is considered is the type of person who would attempt to explain by citing *E*. The contemporary cosmologist may say there are two explanations, since what he is counting as explanations are only *E*'s actually proposed by leading scientists of the day. Some historians of science may count $E$'s proposed by scientists influential in the nineteenth and twentieth centuries. Still others might be counting $E$'s that no actual person would have proposed but that it is plausible to imagine someone as being willing to propose.

The definition of explanation can also be relativized to the situation $S$, since whether $A$ would attempt to explain $q$ by citing $E$ depends on the knowledge and concerns of those to whom he would attempt to explain. The notion of *someone* attempting to explain something *to someone else* is central for a definition of explanation. There are other uses of the concept of attempting to explain, but these are derivative. Thus, textbooks in science are said to attempt to explain and may do so without including information about the knowledge and concerns of those who might read them. But this would not be true unless it is the authors of these texts who are attempting to explain. And the authors consider, at least in a general sort of way, the background and training of their potential readers as well as the sorts of questions, puzzles, or unclarities such persons are likely to have. They attempt to explain for persons with certain knowledge and concerns. $S$ need not always be describable in a precise way, nor need the class of persons referred to have the same background and interests in order that $A$ be said to be attempting to explain $q$ to them.

With this in mind let me propose the following definition:

III. Given $C$, the context of classification, $E$ is classifiable as being or providing an explanation of $q$, within situation $S$, if and only if there is (was, might have been) some (type of) $A$ who would attempt to explain $q$ to those in $S$ by citing $E$ or by citing a number of things of which $E$ is the most central. Whether we choose 'is', 'was', or 'might have been', and what type of $A$ is allowed (e.g. leading scientist $A$), depends on $C$.

Does this open the flood-gates for explanations? In one sense, Yes. Given many $E$'s and $q$'s that to us seem quite unrelated, we can at least imagine an $A$ and a situation $S$ such that $A$ would attempt to explain $q$ to those in $S$ by citing $E$. But this would make $E$ an explanation only relative to that situation and that context of classification. It would not necessarily make it an explanation given a context in which we are considering what $E$'s leading contemporary scientists would cite in explaining $q$ and actual situations in which they would do so. My point is that we need a definition of 'explanation' that will permit such flexibility in what can and cannot be counted as an explanation. Sometimes our criterion is narrow, sometimes not.

## 3. Understanding

Since 'explanation' is defined by reference to 'explain', and this in turn by reference to 'understanding', I will need to consider the latter. To do so it will be useful to refer to some work of Sylvain Bromberger.[1] Let us begin with a pair of examples analogous to ones Bromberger employs. In the first example, I do not know how cells divide; but worse, any hypothesis I can conceive regarding how cells divide is precluded by what I know or believe, or is incorrect, or both. (Under 'conceive' Bromberger includes activities such as imagine, conjure up, invent, and remember.)[2] In the second example, again I do not know how cells divide, but this time I can at least conceive of hypotheses regarding cell division none of which is precluded by what I know or believe, or one of which is correct, or both. In both of these cases I do not know how cells divide. However, according to Bromberger, in the first case, but not the second, I do not understand how cells divide.

More generally, Bromberger's account can be expressed as follows. Let $Q$ be some question and $q$ the *oratio obliqua* form of $Q$. Any statement of the form '$A$ does not understand $q$' (e.g. '$A$ does not understand how cells divide')

may be used to report or describe situations in which *either* (1) none of the answers that the person mentioned at '$A$' can conceive is an answer that that person can accept—and this includes situations in which the person spoken about can conceive of the right answer, but cannot accept it in the light of his or her other beliefs—*or* (2) none of the answers that the person mentioned at '$A$' can conceive is the right answer—and this includes situations in which that person can conceive of one or more answers that he or she can consistently accept. These statements are thus marked by an ambiguity, and demand contextual clues that indicate whose conditions on the answer are at play, the speaker's or those of the person spoken about.[3]

To extend this account to '$A$ does not understand $q$' where $q$ is not a question in *oratio obliqua* form (e.g. understanding phenomena, events, facts), Bromberger suggests that the $q$ is always replaceable by a suitable question or set of questions in this form.

[1] 'An Approach to Explanation', *Analytical Philosophy*, ed. R. J. Butler (Oxford, 1965), ii. 72–105.    [2] Ibid., p. 82.

[3] Ibid., p. 83. If condition (1) obtains and $A$ also believes that $Q$ admits of a right answer, then $A$ is in what Bromberger calls a $p$-predicament with regard to $Q$ (p. 82). If condition (2) obtains and $Q$ in fact admits of a right answer, then $A$ is in what Bromberger calls a $b$-predicament with regard to $Q$ (p. 90). Bromberger goes on to propose a definition of '$A$ explained $q$ to $B$' which uses the concepts of $p$- and $b$-predicaments and is different from my account in important respects; e.g. it is concerned only with good explanations.

This analysis contains some valuable ideas, but there are also some difficulties, as illustrated by the following examples.

(i) Suppose John, who listened to Mary, thinks she said 'I love you' when she really said 'isle of view'. We might then conclude that John does not understand what Mary said, even though neither of Bromberger's conditions (1) or (2) holds; i.e. even though (1) John can conceive of an answer to the question 'What did Mary say?' that he can accept (though it is not correct) and (2) John can even conceive of the right answer (though he cannot accept it).

(ii) Suppose John knows that a certain prisoner escaped by sliding underneath the door of his cell. He can accept this as a correct answer to the question 'How did the prisoner escape?' because, let us say, he actually saw the prisoner escape in this manner. But he finds it very puzzling, very implausible, in the sense that it is so inconsonant with his other beliefs. If so, we might say that although he accepts as correct a certain answer to the question 'How did the prisoner escape?', and that answer is correct, he does not understand how the prisoner escaped. On Bromberger's analysis, however, we are debarred from saying this, since neither condition (1) nor (2) is satisfied. To be sure, there is also a sense in which we might say that John understands how the prisoner escaped (after all he knows that he escaped by sliding underneath the door). What Bromberger's scheme seems not to allow for is the former sense of not understanding.

One might reply in Bromberger's defence that what John does not understand is how the prisoner slid underneath the door, not how the prisoner escaped. But to this the proper rejoinder is that in so far as John does not understand how the prisoner slid underneath the door he does not understand how the prisoner escaped. At any rate there is a problem here that Bromberger's analysis does not satisfactorily resolve, and I shall return to it subsequently. The general point is that someone may have a very strong, even decisive, reason $r$ for believing that a certain answer to a question $Q$ is correct, even though that answer is inconsonant with other views he holds. He may accept that answer as correct on the basis of $r$, *despite* his other views. If so, there is a sense in which although he accepts an answer to $Q$ as correct, which indeed it is, he does not understand $q$, simply because the answer is inconsonant with other views he holds.

There is a further problem. Bromberger does not attempt to explicate '$A$ understands $q$', and, from what he says, it is not clear that we can simply take the negation of his explication of '$A$ does not under-

F

stand *q*'. Consider the question: 'Is Concord the capital of New Hampshire?' Suppose I know the correct answer. If so, then at least one of the answers I can conceive is an answer I can accept, and at least one of the answers I can conceive is the right answer. So neither of Bromberger's conditions (1) or (2) holds for me. Can we conclude from this that I understand whether Concord is the capital of New Hampshire? What Bromberger says appears to disallow speaking of understanding in such a case, since he claims that we cannot say that someone does not understand this. Accordingly, even if what Bromberger says about not understanding could be accepted, his account does not seem to settle the question of what it means to assert that *A* understands *q*.

In what follows, then, I want to propose an alternative account of understanding. I shall treat 'understanding' rather than 'not understanding' as the more fundamental notion and propose conditions that are satisfied if *A* understands *q* (where *q* is the *oratio obliqua* form of a question *Q*). The conditions that follow are not independent of each other. But it will be useful to formulate them as I do so that later we may be able to consider ways in which *A* might not understand *q*.

(1) *Q* is a sound question and *A* believes that it is. (By a sound question I mean one that admits of a correct answer that does not challenge the legitimacy of the question.) It is inappropriate to describe a certain physicist as understanding why atomic nuclei contain no neutral particles if in fact they do. There might be a theory which says that atomic nuclei contain no neutral particles and our physicist might understand this theory. But from this we cannot conclude that he understands why atomic nuclei contain no neutral particles. Moreover, if *A* does not believe that *Q* is a sound question then he cannot be said to understand *q*. If an astronomer believes that the earth was not formed from the sun, then we cannot say that he understands how the earth was formed from the sun.

(2) *A* has at least some acquaintance with the item(s) mentioned in, or presupposed by, *Q*. If *A* understands the manner in which electrons revolve about the atomic nucleus, then he is aware that there are electrons, that there is an atomic nucleus, and that the former do revolve about the latter. If *q* is what is or was said or meant by something or someone when a sentence, statement, word, or concept was used, then *A* is aware that the sentence, statement, word, concept was used. If I am not aware that anyone spoke, I cannot be

described as understanding what someone said when he spoke. This condition is not implied by the first one, since, e.g. a layman who has never studied physics may believe on the authority of the physicist that a certain question $Q$ in physics is sound, even though he is not acquainted with the item(s) mentioned in, or presupposed by, $Q$.

(3) (The third condition is more complex, so I shall state it first in an 'idealized' form without certain necessary qualifications.) $A$ knows an answer to $Q$ that is correct and that is consonant with his other views; he knows, and therefore believes, that this answer is correct and that it is consonant with his other views; and he knows what the answer means. If $A$ does not know an answer to the question 'How was the solar system formed?' that is correct then he does not understand how the solar system was formed. Even if he knows an answer that is correct, but that answer is not consonant with his other views, this counts against the claim that he understands. Recall the earlier example in which someone knows an answer to the question $Q$ 'How did the prisoner escape?' that is correct (he slid underneath the door) but does not understand $q$, since the answer is not consonant with his other views. If $A$ knows an answer to 'How did the prisoner escape?' which happens to be correct though $A$ believes that it is not, or if $A$ believes that such an answer is not consonant with his other views, then either of these facts would also count against the claim that $A$ understands how the prisoner escaped.

In short, understanding involves not only knowledge of a correct answer but also knowledge that this answer is consonant with one's other beliefs. Normally these two sorts of knowledge go together, and we do not bother to distinguish them. But, as the prisoner example shows, there can be occasions when if one is present without the other we refrain from speaking of understanding. It is sometimes said that understanding involves integration of knowledge. The present condition is intended to bring out what I regard as important in this claim. Integrated knowledge, in the sense in which it is relevant for understanding, involves knowing correct answers and knowing that they fit in with other answers one takes to be correct.

Having stated this third condition rather boldly, even suggesting that there is a sharp distinction between understanding and not understanding, some qualifications are in order. To begin with, here and earlier I have spoken of consonance, which can be construed in terms of probability in the light of one's views. $p$ is consonant with $A$'s views to the extent that $A$'s views do not make $p$ improbable.

Since consonance admits of degrees, what we should say is this: If $A$ knows that a certain answer to $Q$ is a correct one, but that answer is not consonant with his (other) views, to the extent that it is not, or to the extent that it is not according to $A$, he does not (fully) understand $q$.

Understanding admits of degrees in other respects. Many questions can be regarded as answered correctly on different levels, and with varying amounts of completeness, unification, and accuracy.[1] So we may also speak of how deep, complete, unified, and accurate $A$'s understanding of $q$ is. How much depth etc. is required in order to say simply that $A$ understands $q$ depends on standards appropriate for the context in which the judgement is made. There are contexts in which such standards are not very stringent. If $A$ knows an answer to $Q$ that can be regarded as correct, even though it is not consonant with his other views, or $A$ does not know or believe that it is, then $A$'s understanding is not very complete, or deep, or unified. There are contexts in which this would not prevent an attribution of understanding to $A$. Recall that in the prisoner example I granted that there is a sense in which we might say that John understands how the prisoner escaped even though the answer he believes correct is not consonant with his other beliefs. What this means is that there are contexts not calling for (very much) depth, completeness, or unification in the answers to questions. To say that there is a sense in which John does *not* understand how the prisoner escaped is to say that there are contexts calling for greater depth, completeness, or unification. In such contexts the fact that the answer John believes correct is not consonant with his other views means that the answer does not provide sufficient depth, completeness, or unification to warrant the claim that he understands.

Condition (3), then, might more properly be understood as follows: $A$ knows an answer to $Q$ that can be regarded as correct; how accurate, deep, complete, and unifying this answer needs to be to say that $A$ understands $q$ can vary and depends on standards appropriate for the context of evaluation. If the answer is not consonant with $A$'s other views, or if $A$ does not know or believe that it is, then this can count against saying that he understands $q$, depending on (a) the extent of the inconsonance, and (b) standards of depth, completeness, and unification that are appropriate for the context.

(4) To express the fourth condition requires a distinction between

[1] See section 4.

two types of questions. Some (sound) questions are of a type such that if someone were unable to conceive of an answer to a question of this type which is not inconsonant with his views,[1] the natural inference is that he does not believe the question is (completely) sound, or he does not (fully) know what the question means, or he can conceive of several answers to the question, knows that one of them (but not which) is correct, and yet none is consonant with his views. Examples of such questions are: 'How many people are there is this room?', 'How high is Mont Blanc?', 'Is Concord the capital of New Hampshire?' Someone might not know correct answers to such questions. But if he cannot even conceive of any possible answer to them which is not inconsonant with his views, then the natural inference is that one of the previous conditions obtains. If someone cannot conceive of an answer to the question 'Is Concord the capital of New Hampshire?' that is not inconsonant with his views, either he believes the question unsound (e.g. he thinks New Hampshire is a city); or he does not know what it means; or he can conceive of several answers, knows that one of them is correct, yet none is consonant with (all) his views (e.g. he believes that atlases provide reliable information about state capitals yet has read in one that Concord is the capital of New Hampshire and in another that Manchester is).

If $Q$ is a question of this type then, one might be tempted to conclude, we would not say that $A$ understands $q$, even if he knows an answer to $Q$ that is correct and consonant with his views (cf. Bromberger). For example, '$A$ knows how high Mont Blanc is' sounds perfectly proper, '$A$ understands how high Mont Blanc is' sounds less so. But such a conclusion is too hasty. Someone who sees $A$ about to climb Mont Blanc with no equipment might say '$A$ does not understand how high Mont Blanc is'. We might reply 'He understands how high it is', and by doing so either rebut the suggestion that he cannot conceive that it might be more than 15,000 feet high, or claim that he recognizes the significance or implications of the fact that it is so high, or both. In general, if $Q$ is a question of the present type we could say that $A$ understands $q$ only if either (1) we are rebutting the suggestion that $A$ not only does not know an answer to $Q$ that is correct and consonant with his views but that he cannot conceive of such an answer (either because he cannot conceive of the answer

---

[1] This includes the case in which he is unable to conceive of any answer at all as well as the case in which he is able to conceive of answers but all are inconsonant with his views.

which is correct, or, if he can, because that answer is so completely inconsonant with his views that he could not take it seriously), or (2) if we are making the claim that *A* recognizes the significance or implications of the fact that such and such an answer to *Q* is correct.

There is another type of question, however. This type of question is such that from the mere fact that someone is unable to conceive of an answer that is not inconsonant with his views, we are not entitled to infer that he does not believe the question sound, or does not know what it means, or can conceive of several answers, knows that one (but not which) is correct, but none is consonant with his views. If someone cannot conceive of an answer to the question 'How was the solar system formed?' that is not inconsonant with his views we are not automatically entitled to draw this conclusion. For example, such a person may believe the question is sound, may know what it means, yet may not be able to generate answers to it, or may not be able to generate answers and know that among these is a correct one. If *Q* is such a question, it is not at all odd to say that *A* understands *q*. And if we do say this we are not necessarily rebutting the suggestion or making the claim described in the previous paragraph.

According to the present condition, then, if it is correct to say that *A* understands *q*, then either *Q* is a question of the second type, or, if it is a question of the first type then '*A* understands *q*' is being used either to rebut a suggestion that *A* does not know and cannot conceive of an answer to *Q* that is correct and consonant with his views or to say that *A* recognizes the significance or implications of the fact that such and such an answer to *Q* is correct.

I have suggested four conditions typically satisfied if *A* understands *q*. What can we say about *not* understanding *q*? If any of these conditions are not satisfied then it is not the case that *A* understands *q*. If the fourth condition is satisfied, the non-satisfaction of any of the first three can be sufficient for saying that *A* does not understand *q*. Thus, if *Q* is unsound we may conclude that *A* does not understand *q*. If a physicist claims to understand why atomic nuclei contain no neutral particles, we might reply that he does not understand *q* at all. More typically, however, the conditions under which we speak of not understanding are stricter. More typically, when we say '*A* does not understand *q*' we imply or presuppose that conditions (1), (2), and (4) for understanding, but not condition (3), are satisfied, and furthermore that *A* is not in the position of being able to conceive of several answers to *Q* that are consonant with his views, knowing that one is correct but not which. If someone claimed that $A$ does not understand how cells divide the likely implication of such a claim would be that cells do divide and $A$ believes they do, that $A$ has some acquaintance with cells (he knows something about them), that $Q$ is a question of the second type described in condition (4), and that $A$ is not in the position of being able to conceive of several answers to the question 'How do cells divide?' that are consonant with his views, knowing that one of them is correct but not which.

I think that we use '$A$ does not understand $q$' in both ways described above, i.e. (a) where not satisfying one of the first three conditions for understanding $q$ but satisfying the fourth is sufficient for not understanding $q$, or (b) where not satisfying the third condition but satisfying the others is sufficient, provided that $A$ is not in the position of being able to conceive of several answers to $Q$ that are consonant with his views, knowing that one is correct but not which. In the former sense we can say that Lincoln did not understand why President Kennedy was assassinated, in the latter sense we cannot. It might be said that (b) represents a more strict and proper use of '$A$ does not understand $q$', whereas (a) should be read 'It is not the case that $A$ understands $q$'. But perhaps this is over-rigid.

If I am right, then, even in sense (b) there are several ways in which $A$ might not understand $q$, i.e. several circumstances in which it would be proper to say that $A$ does not understand $q$. So that we may employ sense (b), suppose we assume that conditions (1), (2), and (4) for understanding are satisfied and that $A$ is not in the position of being able to conceive of several answers to $Q$ that are consonant with his views, knowing that one is correct but not which. Suppose further that $Q$ is a question of the second type described in (4). Given these assumptions, $A$ might be in any one of the following circumstances in virtue of which we could conclude that he does not understand $q$: he might be unable to conceive of any answer to $Q$; he might be able to conceive of several answers to $Q$ but none of which is correct; he might be able to conceive of an answer to $Q$ which is correct but which he believes to be incorrect; he might be unable to conceive of any answer to $Q$ which is consonant with his views; and so forth. As already noted, understanding, and therefore not understanding, admits of degrees. The extent to which someone does not understand $q$ can depend upon the extent to which a correct answer to $Q$ is not consonant with his views. It can also depend upon the extent of his inability to conceive of such an answer. The more difficult *A* finds it to conceive of any answer, or of an answer that is consonant with his views, the greater the lack of understanding we may attribute to him.

Let me return now to explanation. We began with the schema:

I. *A* would attempt to explain *q* to those in situation *S* by citing *E*, or by citing a number of things of which *E* is the most central.

Invoking the concept of understanding, I said that this could be expressed as follows:

II. *A* would attempt to render *q* understandable to those in situation *S* by citing *E*, or a number of things of which *E* is the most central, as providing what *A* believes is or might be a correct answer to *Q*.

I then defined the concept of explanation by reference to schema I, as follows:

III. Given *C*, the context of classification, *E* is classifiable as being or providing an explanation of *q*, within situation *S*, if and only if there is (was, might have been) some (type of) *A* who would attempt to explain *q* to those in *S* by citing *E* or by citing a number of things of which *E* is the most central. Whether we choose 'is', 'was', or 'might have been', and what type of *A* is allowed (e.g. leading scientist *A*) depends on *C*.

Let me now tie schemas I, II, and III to my remarks about understanding.

Suppose *A* is attempting to render *q* understandable to those in *S*, where *q* is the *oratio obliqua* form of a question *Q* of the second type described in condition (4). Appealing to my account of understanding, this means that *A* is attempting to provide a correct answer to *Q* in order to enable those in *S* to satisfy the conditions for understanding described above. It does not necessarily follow that such an attempt will produce understanding of *q* by those in *S*. The answer *A* provides may not be correct, or may not be consonant with the views of those in *S*. Even if it is, once given such an answer those in *S* may not satisfy other conditions for understanding *q*. To produce understanding *A* may need to do more than provide a correct answer to *Q*. He may need to show that *Q* is a sound question. He may need to make those in *S* acquainted with items mentioned in, or presupposed by, *Q*. He may need to modify or augment the views of those in *S* in such a way that the answer becomes consonant with their views. If *A* does provide this additional information we can say, if we wish, that it is part of *A*'s answer to *Q*. Let me call an answer to *Q* which does not contain any of this additional information a *narrow* answer to *Q*, and an answer to $Q$ which does, a *broad* answer to $Q$. To provide a narrow answer to $Q$ is to 'just answer the question', without trying to show that it is sound, saying what it means, trying to show how the answer is consonant with a set of beliefs, and so forth. To provide a broad answer is to do some of these other things as well. In attempting to explain $q$ to those in situation $S$, where $Q$ is a question of the second type described in condition (4), $A$ may cite $E$ as providing either a broad or a narrow answer to $Q$. Depending on the $S$, either a broad or narrow answer to $Q$ may render $q$ understandable to those in $S$. It does not follow, of course, that it will.

Suppose now that $Q$ is a question of the first type described in condition (4). Then we would say that those in $S$ understand $q$ only if we were rebutting the suggestion that they do not know and cannot conceive of an answer to $Q$ that is correct and plausible, i.e. consonant with their views, or if we were claiming that they recognize the significance or implications of the answer that is correct. So if $A$ is attempting to explain $q$ to those in $S$, i.e. if he is attempting to bring them to understand $q$ by citing $E$, the implication may be that not only do those in $S$ not know an answer to $Q$ which is both correct and consonant with their views but that they cannot conceive of such an answer. This may be because they believe $Q$ to be unsound; or because they do not know what it means; or because, although they can conceive of several answers to $Q$ and they know that one of them is correct (but not which), none is consonant with their views; or because the correct answer to $Q$ is so completely inconsonant with their views. Or else the implication may be that those in $S$ do not recognize the significance of the fact that such and such an answer is correct. Accordingly, if $Q$ is a question of the first type described in (4), and we want to say that $E$ is or provides an explanation of $q$, or that $A$ would attempt to explain $q$ by citing $E$, then $E$ contains not only (what $A$ takes to be) a correct and plausible answer to $Q$ but also information provided in the light of the fact that those in $S$ are (assumed to be) in one or more of the circumstances described above. For example, we might say that within $S$, $A$ attempted to explain how high Mont Blanc is by citing $E$, and we might speak of $E$ as being or providing an explanation of this, within $S$. If we do say this, then $E$ will contain more than the information '15,781 feet'. $E$ will contain at least some information purporting to demonstrate the soundness of the question, or to indicate something about Mont Blanc in addition to its height, or to indicate the plausibility of the answer

'15,781 feet', or to indicate the significance of this answer for the prospective climber. The proposition 'Mont Blanc is 15,781 feet high' by itself does not provide an explanation of how high Mont Blanc is. If, e.g., any answer that those in $S$ can conceive to the question 'How high is Mont Blanc?' is an answer that is not plausible, given their views, then we might explain to them how high Mont Blanc is by telling them that it is 15,781 feet and showing them why this figure is plausible (which, of course, will involve changing their views). In short, where $Q$ is a question of the first type described in (4), $E$ will provide a broad rather than a narrow answer to $Q$.

We can bring all this together by writing down the following schema as an analysis of 'explanation':

IV. Given $C$, the context of classification, $E$ is classifiable as being or providing an explanation of $q$, within situation $S$, if and only if there is (was, might have been) some (type of) $A$ such that, within $S$, $A$ would cite $E$ as providing what he believes is or might be a correct answer to $Q$, where $Q$ is a question of the second type described in condition (4), where $E$ provides either a narrow or a broad answer to $Q$, and where $A$ would provide such an answer in order to enable those in $S$ to satisfy the conditions for understanding previously cited; if $Q$ is a question of the first type, then $E$ will provide a broad rather than a narrow answer to $Q$. (Whether we choose 'is', 'was', or 'might have been', and what type of $A$ is allowed, depends on $C$.)

## 4. Evaluating Explanations

What does one evaluate when one evaluates an explanation? The $E$'s I have spoken of as being or providing explanations can be such things as events, facts, phenomena, states of affairs, and propositions. These are items that $A$ can cite in explaining $q$. But when I speak of evaluating an explanation I do not mean evaluating an event, fact, phenomenon, state of affairs, or proposition. What I mean is determining whether by citing one of these items $A$ would be providing a good (satisfactory, illuminating, etc.) explanation of $q$. Following the procedure I have been adopting, this means evaluating $A$'s answer to a question $Q$ in which $E$ is cited in order to render $q$ understandable to those in $S$. To begin with, I shall note several criteria that are important for evaluating an explanation from the point of view of those in the situation $S$ in which the explanation is offered. Afterwards I shall discuss the possibility of making evaluations independently of any $S$.

Persons in $S$ either do not understand $q$ or can be treated as if they do not. What is not understood is, or can be expressed as, the *oratio obliqua* form of a question. However, if a person does not, or can be treated as if he does not, understand *q*, often there will be several questions he might raise in addition to *Q*.[1] If he does not understand why the spectrum of hydrogen contains discrete lines, he might ask how spectra are produced, what the structure of the hydrogen atom is, what general physical principles are involved, and so forth. With this in mind, I want to mention several considerations for deciding whether, by citing *E*, *A* is providing an explanation of *q* that is a good or satisfactory one within *S*.

*R₁*. *Relevance.* By citing *E*, does *A* provide an answer to *Q* and to other questions that are or might be raised by those in *S* who do not, or can be treated as if they do not, understand *q*? Is *A* attempting to render *q* understandable and to do so in respects that are or might be of concern to those in *S*?

*R₂*. *Correctness.* By citing *E* does *A* provide a correct answer to *Q* as well as to other questions that are or might be raised by those in *S* who do not understand *q*? How correct the answers need to be, or what amounts to the same thing, what counts as a correct answer, depends on standards appropriate for the situation: in some cases approximations, simplifications, idealizations are in order, in others not. Related criteria are evidential support and simplicity. (By citing *E* does *A* provide evidentially well-supported and simple answers to questions that are or might be raised in *S*?) Both of these are relevant in considering whether an explanation is correct, and each is used for purposes of evaluation.

*R₃*. *Depth.* By citing *E* at what level does *A* provide an answer to *Q* and to other questions that are or might be raised by those in *S* who do not understand *q*? Even though *A* does answer such questions, and his answers are correct (as far as they go), we may say that his explanation is shallow or superficial if we think that more fundamental considerations should have been adduced. Thus, although one can explain why gases at constant pressure expand by citing a temperature increase, a deeper answer would appeal to the molecular constitution of gases.

*R₄*. *Completeness.* By citing *E* how completely, at a given level, does *A* answer *Q* and other questions that are or might be raised by those in *S* who do not understand *q*? Even though *A* may attempt to answer

[1] This will always be true if *Q* is a question of the first type noted in condition (4) of the previous section.

questions about pressure at the microscopic level, instead of the macroscopic (thermodynamic) level, his answers at the more fundamental level may be quite sketchy.

$R_5$. *Unification.* To what extent does the citing of $E$ provide unification for the items concerning which questions are or might be raised by those in $S$ who do not understand $q$? An explanation may be given high marks in virtue of the fact that a few ideas bring together a wide range of items, relationships among which would otherwise be unknown or not considered.

$R_6$. *Manner of Presentation.* When $A$ presents his explanation does he do so in a sufficiently clear, simple, and organized manner so as to be likely to render $q$ understandable to persons in $S$?

Here, then, are a number of criteria for evaluating explanations from the point of view of those in $S$. Many terms of evaluation can be tied to one or more of them. We may speak of an explanation as a powerful one, on the basis of the unification it provides and in addition its depth. If we say that an explanation is illuminating we may have in mind several criteria, especially relevance, depth, unification, and manner of presentation. If we say that it is plausible, we will be employing criteria such as evidential support and simplicity mentioned under correctness, and also perhaps unification. This is not to deny that certain terms, e.g. 'original', 'imaginative', and 'influential', not tied to any of the criteria above can be used to evaluate explanations. I have not exhausted the dimensions in which evaluations are possible.

How are $R_1$,..., $R_6$ to be used? When we evaluate an explanation we may do so only in certain respects. We may say that the Ptolemaic explanation of the motions of the planets is a good one with respect to completeness and unification, although it is not correct. Now within $S$ an explanation satisfies $R_1$ if and only if it provides an answer to $Q$ and to other questions that are or might be raised by those in $S$ who do not understand $q$; it satisfies $R_2$ if and only if it supplies correct answers; and so on. What counts as relevant, how much accuracy, depth, completeness, or unification is appropriate, and what type of presentation is in order, depends on, and varies with, the knowledge and concerns of those in $S$. We evaluate $E$ with respect to $R_i$ by considering what standard of $R_i$ is appropriate in $S$ and then determining how $E$ measures up to that standard. So we can say:

A. Given the knowledge and concerns of those in $S$, $E$ is or provides an explanation of $q$ which is a good (satisfactory) one, within $S$, with respect to $R_i$ (relevance, correctness, etc.) if and only if $E$ is classifiable as an explanation of $q$ within $S$ and $E$ satisfies $R_i$ to an extent appropriate in $S$.

Sometimes we are willing to evaluate an explanation not simply with respect to individual criteria but 'on the whole', i.e. taking all the criteria into account. One thing we can say is this:

**B.** Where $E$ is classifiable as an explanation of $q$ within $S$, the more criteria appropriate to $S$ which $E$ satisfies, and the greater the extent to which it satisfies them to the level appropriate to $S$, the better $E$ is as an explanation of $q$ within $S$.

If, however, given $S$, we want a schema for an 'absolute' evaluation of $E$ on the whole, the matter becomes much less precise. Possibly we attach varying degrees of importance to the criteria cited, but how we do this, and combine such information with that indicating the extent to which $E$ satisfies each criterion, is not at all clear. So, quite vaguely, supposing now that $R_1, ..., R_6$ represent a sufficient number of criteria to evaluate $E$ on the whole, we can say this:

**C.** Where $E$ is classifiable as an explanation of $q$ within $S$, $E$ is, on the whole, a good or satisfactory explanation of $q$, within $S$, if and only if, on the whole, $E$ satisfies the $R_1, ..., R_6$ appropriate to $S$.

An ideal explanation with respect to $R_1, ..., R_6$, within $S$, might be defined thus:

**D.** Where $E$ is classifiable as an explanation of $q$, within $S$, $E$ is an ideal explanation of $q$, within $S$, if and only if $E$ satisfies each of the $R_1, ..., R_6$ appropriate in $S$ to the fullest extent appropriate in $S$.

I have spoken about evaluating an explanation given the knowledge and concerns of those in $S$. Can we evaluate an explanation independently of any $S$? It might be argued that we can, at least to a large extent. True, it might be said, to evaluate $E$ one must consider the question $Q$ that $E$ purports to be answering. And this question itself indicates at least something about the knowledge and concerns of those in a situation $S$. The question partially defines such a situation. But we can determine whether $E$ provides an answer to $Q$ that is relevant, correct, etc., without very fully specifying $S$. We can judge that one explanation is deeper than another by specifying a question it is attempting to answer, without indicating anything further about any $S$.[1]

[1] It might be objected that this is not really consistent with the policy of relativizing the definition of explanation to an $S$. So two moves might be made. When we consider the extent to which $E$ satisfies $R_i$ we might assume that $E$ is

The problem is that given just $Q$ we cannot always determine the level of $R_i$ that is appropriate, and this is necessary for evaluating $E$. Given just $Q$ we may be able to say that $E_1$ is a deeper explanation than $E_2$. But can we conclude that it is better? Can we give $E_1$ higher marks, even if $E_1$ and $E_2$ are equal in other respects? The answer depends upon what level of depth is appropriate in $S$, which in turn depends on the knowledge and concerns of those in $S$, something not necessarily indicated by $Q$. An explanation of a blow-out in an automobile tyre that makes reference to kinetic theory is deeper than one appealing only to the expansion of the air as a result of temperature increase. But it is not necessarily better. Here we do have to consider the knowledge and concerns of those in $S$, information not fully indicated by the question 'Why did the tyre blow-out?' The deeper explanation is not always the better one. Similar remarks apply to completeness and unification. With relevance and correctness matters are somewhat different, for in all situations these are important in evaluating an explanation on the whole. Still, what counts as relevant depends upon $S$, and what standard of correctness is appropriate varies with the situation. Finally, what manner of presentation is appropriate will also depend to some extent on $S$. In certain situations a rigorous axiomatic presentation may be in order, in others a much less formal, and more 'intuitive' one.[1]

It might be objected that explanations in science, at least, can be evaluated knowing just the questions they are attempting to answer. Since science aims at correctness, depth, completeness, and unification, the more accurate, deep, complete, and unifying explanation is always the better one, scientifically speaking.

In science, to be sure, the situations presupposed when explanations are given are considerably standardized. A text in kinetic theory does not offer a different explanation of gaseous phenomena for each reader with a different interest and background. Rather it presupposes over-all uniformity in its audience with respect to knowledge and interests. Nevertheless, different texts will develop kinetic theory at different levels, with varying degrees of accuracy, depth, completeness, and unification; even the same text may do so in different chapters. Most important, it is simply untrue that we can evaluate

to count as an explanation of $q$ within some $S$, which is not further specified. Or we might speak of $E$ as a potential explanation of $q$ and judge that one potential explanation is deeper than another, independently of any $S$.

[1] See my *Concepts of Science*, chapter 4.

an explanation of $q$, even in science, just by considering the explanation and the $q$. The appropriate level of correctness, depth, and completeness must be considered as well. At least three factors are responsible for this. In science there is often a quest for simplicity in explanation, for familiarity, and for variety. Each of these can affect the amount of accuracy, depth, completeness, and unification that is appropriate, which in turn affects our evaluation of the explanation.

For example, in kinetic theory, why monatomic gases have the specific heats they do can be explained by ignoring rotation of molecules, collisions between molecules, and quantum mechanical effects, although all of these exist. The explanation proceeds by treating gas molecules as structureless mass points with translational energy only. Admittedly, it provides an answer that describes gases in a manner that is not very accurate, complete, or deep. Still, these additional factors have little effect on the specific heats of monatomic gases. In many scientific situations what is wanted is a simple explanation that takes into account the principal factors only. This is not to deny that in some scientific situations greater accuracy, depth, or completeness may be required. It is also typical in science to approach an issue from several points of view. In explaining transport phenomena, i.e. viscosity, heat conduction, and diffusion in gases, the physicist may use mean-free-path methods based on the idea of a billiard ball model in which molecules travel certain distances (free paths) between collisions. He may use momentum-transfer methods in which the net transfer of momentum during molecular collisions is considered. Or he may use methods based on the distribution of molecular velocities. Each of these explanations can provide important insights concerning transport phenomena, and texts on kinetic theory frequently include all of them. The first two have the advantages of simplicity and familiarity, the latter is more rigorous. Which explanation to rate as the best depends on the knowledge and concerns of those in the situation in which it is to be invoked.

This is not to deny that we do speak of certain scientific explanations as good ones without specifying a situation in which they are given. We may say that the kinetic-theory explanation of transport phenomena is a good one, without mentioning a situation. In this case, however, several explanations, at different levels and even with different assumptions, may all be called 'kinetic-theory explanations', and how these are to be evaluated depends in part on the situation in which they are to be given. Saying that the kinetic-theory explanation of transport phenomena is a good one may simply be a way of saying that some explanation(s) involving kinetic theory can be judged to be good within certain types of situations. When we evaluate an explanation the situation in question need not always be explicitly indicated since it may be obvious in the context in which we make the judgement. Finally, scientists do aim at accuracy, depth, completeness, and unification, and when we evaluate an explanation by reference to these criteria we may have in mind some 'ideal' type of situation in which explanations satisfying these criteria to a 'maximal' extent are appropriate. But by no means all situations in which scientific explanations are given are 'ideal' ones and, in general, the fact that one explanation is more accurate, deeper, more complete, or more unifying than another does not, without at least implicit appeal to a type of situation, permit us to say that it is a better explanation. It permits us to say only that in, or relative to, certain situations it is a better explanation.

# V. Laws and Explanation

## 1. Some Ways that Laws Provide Explanations

A general definition of the concept of explanation has been proposed and various criteria for evaluating explanations suggested. I turn now to the specific problem of the role of laws in explanations. There is a standard view, to be discussed in section 4, which claims that laws, or at least general statements of some sort, must be part of an explanation and must, together possibly with other propositions, deductively entail a statement describing what is to be explained. Even if this view were right in its claims, more needs to be said about the characteristics of laws in virtue of which they can function to provide explanations. On the basis of the previous chapter we can say that a law, or a set of propositions containing a law, can be used to explain something by providing an answer to a question or set of questions. What questions do laws typically provide answers for, how do they do so, and is all the information contained in the law relevant for the answer?

In chapter I, I said that a law attempts to express a regularity underlying other regularities; that it attempts to do so with a certain amount of completeness by isolating various factors that are involved and by indicating how they are related; and that it attempts to formulate the regularity in a precise manner, often quantitatively. A law may be used to furnish an explanation of certain regularities by exposing a deeper, underlying regularity. Often the question for which the explanation supplies an answer is simply 'What is the underlying regularity?' However, we can also focus upon various aspects of a law in virtue of which it can be used to answer more specific questions about aspects of the regularities to be explained. We can isolate certain features of a regularity which a law expresses and appeal to one or more of these in furnishing explanations. For example, we might distinguish (1) some fundamental theoretical idea a law introduces, which underlies the more superficial regularities and which allows the basic regularity to be expressed, from (2) (other) factors the law isolates, and these in turn from (3) the precise, often quantitative, manner in which it relates these factors. Newton's law of gravitation introduces the theoretical idea of a gravitational force of attraction between all bodies, it isolates the factors of mass and distance (in addition to force) as being involved in the regularity, and it provides a quantitative expression of the relationship between these factors. If a question is raised and a law is invoked to supply an answer, then depending on the question and on the situation in which it is raised, one of these aspects of the law may be more central than others in supplying that answer. Let us consider some examples.

(A) Suppose the following questions are raised: What causes unsupported bodies to fall? The tides to occur? The planets to stay in their orbits? One answer is that according to Newton's law of gravitation there is a gravitational force of attraction between bodies: between the earth and bodies near it causing them to fall toward it if not restrained by a counterbalancing force; between the sun, the moon, and water on the earth, causing the latter to rise at certain times; between the sun and the planets, causing them to fall toward it away from their rectilinear paths. Such an answer, which appeals to the idea of gravitational attraction introduced in Newton's law, will in certain situations provide an appropriate explanation, even though reference is not made to the factors of mass and distance and to how they are related, information also provided by the law. An explanation may suffice which appeals only to the general theoretical idea of gravitational attraction, a basic regularity exemplified in the regularities of falling bodies, the tides, and planetary motion.

Suppose it is asked why an oar partially immersed in water looks bent. One answer might be that according to Snell's law, light rays are bent when entering a denser medium, and in this case light is travelling from air into water. Here there is appeal to Snell's law, even though full use of that law is not made. There is no explicit mention of the various factors isolated by the law, i.e. the sines of the angles of incidence and refraction and the index of refraction, or of how these are related, all of which is indicated in Snell's law. Appeal is made only to a central theoretical idea in the law, the bending of light rays, an underlying regularity exemplified in the 'bent oar' regularity. This appeal may suffice in a given situation to answer the question concerning the appearance of the oar correctly and with appropriate depth and completeness, so that the explanation is satisfactory for that situation. In such cases reference is not made to aspects (2) and (3) of the law, or if it is, these aspects are irrelevant or not very central for the answer. The explanatory power of the law derives from a basic theoretical idea associated with aspect (1).

(B) Some questions raised in certain situations call for an answer in which what is central are the various factors isolated by a law. A hollow opaque body with a small opening is almost a perfect absorber of radiation, or black body, which also emits radiatio:.. What factors does the intensity of the radiation emitted depend on? One answer is that according to the Stefan–Boltzmann law, the intensity depends on the temperature of the body and not on factors such as the shape of the enclosure or the material of which the body is made. This is what the law implies, and it is this aspect of the law, and not the information regarding the precise quantitative relationship between radiation and temperature that is central in providing the answer required in this case.

Or consider Coulomb's law of force of torsion of a metal wire. By applying a force to a metal wire we can twist the wire through some particular angle. What factors does the force required to achieve a particular angle depend upon? According to a law of Coulomb, it depends on the length of the wire, its diameter, the angle in question, and on the modulus of rigidity which is a constant for each type of metal. Of course in formulating the law Coulomb was concerned with more than just isolating these factors. He wanted to determine exactly how they are related, and this is something his law states explicitly. Nevertheless, the law can be invoked to answer the question that is being raised, and this aspect of the law may be central in providing an explanation.

(C) Some questions raised in certain situations call for an answer in which the quantitative aspect of the law plays the most central role. The information needed is not simply or primarily some basic theoretical idea which the law contains in terms of which regularities are to be analysed, or factors involved in these regularities which the law isolates. What is important is how such factors are related quantitatively and what mathematical consequences follow from this relationship. Suppose it is asked why, according to Newton's second law of motion, a projectile when hurled forward will follow a parabolic path. And suppose the situation is one in which it is assumed that the various factors isolated by Newton's law—force, mass, and acceleration—are known and that the theoretical idea that forces are responsible for changes in velocity and not for uniform motion is understood. In this situation the explanation might proceed as follows.

Newton's second law can be expressed in terms of component equations of motion involving the rectangular coordinates $x$, $y$, and $z$: $m\ddot{x} = F_x$, $m\ddot{y} = F_y$, $m\ddot{z} = F_z$. If we consider the projectile to be a particle of mass $m$ in a uniform gravitational field, $F_y$, the force acting upon the projectile in the $y$ direction, is $-mg$, where $g$ is the gravitational constant. $F_x$, the force on the projectile in the $x$ direction, is 0, once the projectile is released. If we treat this as a two-dimensional problem, from the component equations we obtain the following equations of motion for the projectile:

$$m\ddot{x} = 0,$$

$$m\ddot{y} = -mg.$$

We integrate these with respect to time and obtain

$$\dot{x} = v_0 \cos A,$$

$$\dot{y} = -gt + v_0 \sin A.$$

$v_0$ is the initial velocity of the projectile when released and $A$ is the angle at which it is released. By integrating the above equations, plugging in appropriate values for $x$, $y$, $\dot{x}$, $\dot{y}$, when $t = 0$, and eliminating $t$ between the last two equations, we obtain

$$y = -\frac{g}{2v_0^2 \cos^2 A} x^2 + x \tan A.$$

This is the path the projectile follows, and the curve described by the equation is a parabola.

In this explanation use is made of Newton's second law, but in the situation I have in mind the important aspect of the law is the quantitative one. Attention is given to the equations expressing the law and to the mathematical derivation of consequences of these equations. I am supposing that such an explanation is being offered in a situation in which it is assumed that the fundamental theoretical idea of the law is understood and that various factors isolated by the law are known.

Cases have been considered in which a law is cited to explain regularities by exposing some deeper, more general regularity which they exemplify. Various features of the underlying regularity can be distinguished, and I have focused on three aspects of laws any of which, in a given case, may be more central than the others in providing an explanation by supplying an answer to a given question. However, it should be emphasized that there will be cases in which these aspects are equally central. An explanation citing Newton's second law might be given of why projectiles follow parabolic paths, and all three aspects of the law might be equally important. Such an explanation might place equal emphasis on the theoretical idea that forces produce changes in velocity, on the factors the law isolates, and on how it relates these mathematically. In many cases all three aspects of laws will be important and the questions raised may not call for the emphasis of one more than another.

## 2. The Compton Effect: A Typical Use of Laws in Explanations

The examples thus far have been fairly simple ones. I turn now to a more complex case, indeed a more typical one, an explanation of the Compton effect. This case brings out some important points about the nature of explanations to which laws frequently contribute.

Compton's experiment showed that when a beam of X-rays of known frequency strikes weakly bound electrons the frequency of the scattered X-rays is less than that of the incident rays, and hence their wavelength is greater. In his 1923 paper Compton begins by pointing out that J. J. Thomson's classical theory of X-ray scattering is incapable of explaining this phenomenon.[1] According to Thomson's theory, an X-ray incident upon an electron should cause the latter to vibrate with a frequency equal to that of the incident ray, which in turn should produce the same frequency in the scattered ray; but this is contradicted by experiment. Compton begins his own explanation of the phenomenon in a qualitative way, by utilizing some ideas of the early quantum theory:

From the point of view of the quantum theory, we may suppose that any particular quantum of X-rays is not scattered by all the electrons in the radiator, but spends all of its energy upon some particular electron. This electron will in turn scatter the ray in some definite direction, at an angle with the incident beam. This bending of the path of the quantum of radiation results in a change in its momentum. As a consequence, the scattering electron will recoil with a momentum equal to the change in momentum of the X-ray. The energy in the scattered ray will be equal to that in the incident ray minus the kinetic energy of the recoil of the scattering electron; and since the scattered ray must be a complete quantum, the frequency will be reduced in the same ratio as is the energy. Thus

[1] A. H. Compton, *Physical Review*, 21 (1923), 483–502.

on the quantum theory we should expect the wavelength of the scattered X-rays to be greater than that of the incident rays.[1]

What Compton is assuming here is that the incident beam contains quanta or photons with quantized energy equal to Planck's constant times the frequency of the radiation. He then treats the scattering as a problem of elastic collision between a photon and an electron, which is subject to the law of conservation of momentum and the law of conservation of energy. The former law is applied by assuming that the scattering electron recoils with a momentum equal to the change in momentum of the X-ray. The latter is involved in the assumption that the energy of the scattered X-ray is equal to that of the incident ray minus the kinetic energy of the recoil electron. The frequency of the photon after collision is less than that before collision because some of the energy has been transferred to the electron, and according to the quantum hypothesis, energy is proportional to frequency.

Following the remarks quoted above, Compton goes on to offer a quantitative explanation of the phenomenon, which can be recast as follows. Let $E_0$ = the energy of the incident X-ray, which according to Planck's hypothesis = $h\nu$ ($h$ is Planck's constant and $\nu$ is frequency), $E_\theta$ = the energy of the X-ray scattered at angle $\theta$; $E_m$ = energy of the recoil electron. Then according to the law of conservation of energy, total energy of a system of particles before collision = total energy after collision, or, as applied to the system in question:

$$E_0 = E_\theta + E_m. \tag{1}$$

The energy of the recoil electron is assumed to be kinetic energy and for this the relativistic equation is used:

$$E_m = mc^2([1/\sqrt{(1-B^2)}]-1), \qquad B = v/c, \tag{2}$$

where $v$ is the velocity of the electron after collision and $c$ is the velocity of light. Since $E = h\nu$, from (1) and (2) we obtain

$$h\nu_0 = h\nu_\theta + mc^2([1/\sqrt{(1-B^2)}]-1). \tag{3}$$

Formula (3) represents the application of the law of conservation of energy to the problem.

The law of conservation of momentum must now be applied, according to which total momentum before collision = total momentum after collision:

$$p_0 = p_\theta + P_m. \tag{4}$$

[1] Ibid., p. 485.

The momentum $p$ of a photon of frequency $v$ is $hv/c$, and the relativistic momentum $P_m$ of the electron after collision is $mv/\sqrt{(1-B^2)}$. The law of conservation of momentum can be written for this situation in two equations, one giving the component of momentum in the direction of propagation of the incident photon, and the other at right angles to it:

$$\frac{hv_0}{c} = \frac{hv_\theta}{c}\cos\theta + \frac{mBc}{\sqrt{(1-B^2)}}\cos\phi, \qquad (5)$$

$$0 = \frac{hv_\theta}{c}\sin\theta - \frac{mBc}{\sqrt{(1-B^2)}}\sin\phi. \qquad (6)$$

$\phi$ is the angle of deflection of the electron after collision. Substituting wavelengths $\lambda_0 = c/v_0$ and $\lambda_\theta = c/v_\theta$ into (5) and (6), and combining these equations with (3), yields

$$\lambda_\theta - \lambda_0 = \frac{h}{mc}(1-\cos\theta), \qquad (7)$$

which indicates that the wavelength $\lambda_\theta$ of the scattered X-ray is greater than the wavelength $\lambda_0$ of the incident ray by an amount $\frac{h}{mc}(1-\cos\theta)$, where $\theta$ is the angle of deflection of the X-ray.

This example illustrates one way in which laws are typically involved in a scientific explanation. A regularity is given which the scientist seeks to explain. Compton has noted a certain regularity in X-ray scattering, viz. that when X-rays are scattered by electrons there is an increase in their wavelength. He explains the regularity by invoking the laws of conservation of energy and momentum which underlie it. What makes this case typical of many actual scientific explanations involving laws are three things.

First, the underlying regularities are exposed by restructuring the problem in a certain way, as a result of theoretical considerations that are not themselves laws. The idea of restructuring the problem in this way may not be evident to one acquainted with the underlying laws, even if he is aware of the theoretical considerations. The originality and force of the explanation consists in putting two and two together. On the basis of the quantum hypothesis, Compton comes to think of X-rays as having a particle-like nature, and this allows him to describe the scattering regularity as one involving colliding particles, viz. photons and electrons.

Second, laws are invoked that underlie the restructured regularity. These laws may be part of a theory in terms of which the original regularity was restructured, or they may be much broader than that theory; they may be laws which impose conditions of adequacy on any theory in that domain. Using quantum-theoretic ideas and restructuring the scattering as a regularity involving elastic particle collisions, Compton can then invoke conservation laws which underlie such collisions. In accordance with these laws he can assume that the total energy and momentum of a system of particles remains the same before and after collision. However, he cannot simply use the laws in this form; he must apply them to the problem at hand, as he does in equations (1) and (4), by relating the energies and the momenta of the particular particles involved. In many explanations in which laws are used an important part of the task consists in determining how to apply the laws to the situation being analysed.

Third, after restructuring the situation and invoking the laws something is demonstrated. Compton does not answer the question of why X-rays suffer an increase in wavelength, or more particularly, why they obey equation (7), simply by citing the fact that, in accordance with the quantum hypothesis, X-rays can be treated as particles and then by invoking the conservation laws. He shows that these assumptions yield (7) as a consequence. He derives (7) from the quantitative application of the laws of conservation of energy and momentum to the problem at hand. Mathematical derivations are typical of many explanations in physics in which laws are invoked. They are given to make explicit the connection between the underlying laws and the regularity to be explained, a connection that otherwise may not be obvious or unquestionable.

In Compton's explanation the connection between conservation laws as applied in (1) and (4) and the regularity described in (7) is by no means evident. In (1) and (4) expressions have to be determined for the energies and momenta of the incident and scattered X-rays and the recoil electron, and this is done using theoretical considerations from the early quantum theory and from relativistic mechanics. This, indeed, is typical in explanations involving laws when derivations are given. Laws are invoked in which certain factors are related to others; according to the law of conservation of energy, total energy of a system of particles before collision = total energy after collision. This is then applied to the particular situation by saying that the energy of the incident X-ray is equal to the energy of the X-ray scattered at angle $\theta$+the energy of the recoil electron, or (1) above. But in order to derive (7) it must be determined what these energies are. This is done by invoking the quantum relationship $E = h\nu$, in the cases of the incident and scattered X-rays, and by invoking the relativistic expression for kinetic energy in the case of the recoil electron. Similar procedures are adopted with respect to the law of conservation of momentum, and the results are combined to generate (7). The reason that the relationship between the underlying laws, as applied in (1) and (4), and the regularity described in (7) is not obvious or unquestionable is because it is by no means evident what the energies and momenta are and how when plugged into the appropriate equations (7) emerges as a consequence.

In section 1, I noted various aspects of laws that may be appealed to in providing explanations. In the type of case presently under discussion the aspects of the laws invoked that are important in providing an explanation can vary. What is important in Compton's initial qualitative explanation are the basic theoretical ideas of the laws; the particular factors the laws isolate and their precise quantitative formulations are not given. However, in the subsequent quantitative explanation of why X-rays suffer an increase in wavelength no one aspect of the laws seems more central than any other. Compton relies on the basic theoretical idea that energy and momentum are conserved, but to derive (7) he must formulate the laws for the particular case in such a way that the factors they isolate are explicit as are the mathematical relationships between them. Emphasis is not placed on one of these features more than on any other. No doubt it could be, in situations in which appropriate questions are raised or in which the audience is aware of certain facts but not others. For example, by analogy with the projectile case in the previous section, the question or situation might call for emphasis solely on the quantitative derivation. But in the absence of such considerations the laws of conservation of energy and momentum function as part of Compton's explanation in virtue of the fact that they expose basic regularities underlying the one in question and do so by isolating and relating various factors involved. The explanation is typical of many in physics because the exposing of underlying regularities occurs as part of a wider intellectual exercise in which the regularity is first restructured using theoretical ideas, underlying laws are invoked, and a demonstration is offered of the connection between these laws and the regularity.

## 3. Laws and the Evaluation of Explanations

Must laws always be invoked in explanations in science for those explanations to be regarded as satisfactory? Do laws help make possible the satisfaction of the criteria of evaluation for explanations discussed in chapter IV? I am not here raising the question of whether explanations must include general statements of some sort or other, a claim that is often made and will be examined in the next section. I am concerned specifically with those general statements in science that are typically classified as laws. It might be argued that such statements are the backbone of a science and must be present at least in those explanations worthy of being called scientific. This position, I shall argue, is too extreme.

There are numerous explanations in science that invoke no laws, and I shall cite two examples supplied by scientists themselves. The first is an explanation of why gases are viscous, i.e. why they exhibit 'internal friction', which is one Maxwell gave in 1860.

. . . when different strata of a gas slide upon one another with different velocities, they act upon one another with a tangential force tending to prevent this sliding, and similar in its results to the friction between two solid surfaces sliding over each other in the same way. The explanation of gaseous friction, according to our hypothesis, is that particles [molecules] having the mean velocity of translation belonging to one layer of the gas, pass out of it into another layer having a different velocity of translation; and by striking against the particles of the second layer, exert upon it a tangential force which constitutes the internal friction of the gas. The whole friction between two portions of a gas separated by a plane surface, depends upon the total action between all the layers on the one side of that surface upon all the layers on the other side.[1]

In this passage Maxwell first introduces the concept of viscosity on the macroscopic level as something involving internal friction between adjacent layers of a gas. He then goes on to offer an explanation of this in molecular terms without invoking any laws. His appeal is simply to the idea that molecules entering a given layer have a different velocity from that of molecules in that layer and so exert a force on those molecules which constitutes the internal friction. Such an explanation, if considered with reference to an appropriate situation in which it is to be offered, can be perfectly satisfactory. Given the question 'Why are gases viscous?' and given a situation calling for a qualitative account of the central theoretical ideas, this explanation

[1] *The Scientific Papers of James Clerk Maxwell*, ed. W. D. Niven (New York, 1965), i. 390.

provides an answer that is relevant, correct, and sufficiently deep and complete to answer questions that are or might be raised by those who do not understand why gases are viscous. This is not to deny that for other situations more may be required. An explanation may be required showing quantitatively how to derive relevant equations. Indeed, when Maxwell discussed viscosity in gases he wanted not only a qualitative explanation but also a demonstration that from kinetic theory the viscosity equation $F = \mu \, du/dz$ can be derived. To derive this equation from kinetic theory use must be made of Newton's second law, even though in Maxwell's qualitative account this law is not invoked. To be sure there are laws that govern molecular motion and there could be explanations of gaseous viscosity (even qualitative ones) in which some of these were cited. My claim is only that in the qualitative explanation Maxwell gives no appeal is made to them.

My second example is J. J. Thomson's explanation of the nature of cathode rays. Fig. 6 is a diagram of a cathode ray tube:

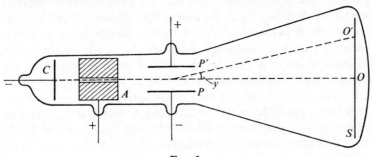

FIG. 6.

$C$ is a cathode, $A$ is the anode with a small hole bored in it, $P$ and $P'$ are parallel plates that can be oppositely charged, and $S$ is a fluorescent screen. If the metal of the cathode is heated or if the cathode is connected to a negative source of high potential and the anode to a positive source, fluorescence is produced on the screen at $O$. When a difference of potential is applied between the plates a fluorescent spot on the screen appears at $O'$. It is natural to suppose that rays—so-called cathode rays—emanate from the cathode, pass through the anode, and then hit the screen causing the fluorescence. How can the nature of these rays be explained? This was the question to which J. J. Thomson addressed himself in 1897.

Thomson notes two possible explanations of these rays. One, proposed by various German physicists, is that they are waves emanating from the cathode. Another explanation, the one defended by Thomson himself, is that this is a corpuscular rather than a wave phenomenon. The rays consist of particles carrying a negative charge, and when there is a difference of potential between the plates these particles, being negatively charged, are deflected toward the positive plate. After considering various experiments with the cathode ray tube, Thomson writes:

> As the cathode rays carry a charge of negative electricity, are deflected by an electrostatic force as if they were negatively electrified, and are acted on by a magnetic force in just the way in which this force would act on a negatively electrified body moving along the path of these rays, I can see no escape from the conclusion that they are charges of negative electricity carried by particles of matter.[1]

The explanation of cathode rays that Thomson offers in this passage as well as in earlier ones invokes no laws. He notes simply that the charged-particle hypothesis rather than the wave hypothesis explains the nature of these rays by explaining their observed behaviour, i.e. the deflection of the rays by electrostatic and magnetic forces. It is certainly true that Thomson did not rest the case here. He wanted to know what sort of particles are involved, whether they are atoms, molecules, or something smaller. To find out he proceeded to derive a formula giving the ratio of the mass of these particles to the charge they carry, and in doing this he made use of the law of conservation of energy. But, just as in the case of Maxwell, Thomson was able to offer a qualitative answer to a question he raised without the introduction of laws.

From these examples it might be concluded that if the scientist seeks a qualitative explanation which cites the main theoretical ideas he need invoke no laws, but if he wants to provide a quantitative explanation involving a derivation of formulae, laws will be necessary. I agree that in many cases this is so, but not in all. Suppose the following question is raised: Given that the path a projectile takes is a parabolic one represented by the equation

$$y = -\frac{g}{2v_0^2 \cos^2 A} x^2 + x \tan A \qquad (1)$$

where $v_0$ is its initial velocity and $A$ is the angle at which it is released,

---

[1] J. J. Thomson, *Philosophical Magazine*, 44 (1897), 293.

why will the horizontal range of the projectile be the farthest if the projectile is released at an angle of 45°? The horizontal range $R$ can be determined by setting $y = 0$ and $x = R$, which yields

$$R = \frac{2v_0^2}{g} \sin A \cos A = \frac{v_0^2}{g} \sin 2A.$$

Now $R$ will be a maximum when $\sin 2A = 1$, which happens when $A = 45°$. In this explanation, which consists of a quantitative derivation, no laws are invoked. Yet given the particular question, the answer provided is relevant, correct, and sufficiently complete for many types of situations to be judged satisfactory. Of course if the question were simply 'Why is a projectile hurled farthest at an angle of 45°?' and if the situation were one in which equation (1) was not given or assumed, then it might be necessary to invoke Newton's second law in explaining why projectiles follow a path described by this equation. My point is only that in view of the question and situation envisaged, invoking Newton's law in order to provide a satisfactory answer is not required, nor would it make the explanation a better one.

Regarding the need for laws in explanations, the most that can be said, I think, is this. Given an explanation which does not explicitly invoke a law, if all the assumptions made in such an explanation were themselves to be explained or justified by appeal to more basic assumptions, and similarly for these in turn, then at some point it is very likely that laws would be invoked. Why is this so? First, if pushed far enough in justifying or explaining assumptions made in an explanation fundamental theories are likely to be invoked whose central and distinctive assumptions may themselves be laws (e.g. Newton's theory of mechanics, Maxwell's theory of the electromagnetic field, or the mechanical theory of heat). Second, even if the central and distinctive assumptions of a theory are not themselves laws, it will often be the case that the theory utilizes laws in its derivations. Being in the typical case quantitative or subject to quantitative formulation, and employing concepts found in many different theories, laws often provide a useful bridge between such theories and quantitative formulae derived with their help. The Bohr theory of the atom can be used to explain why the spectral lines of hydrogen satisfy the Balmer formula.[1] In order to do so, however, in addition to Bohr's two fundamental assumptions regarding quantization of

[1] See chapter I.

angular momentum and energy, use is made of Coulomb's law of electricity, and of Newton's second law of motion. These laws, in addition to the basic assumptions of his theory, allow Bohr to derive the Balmer formula. Third, there are certain very fundamental laws pervading all of physics, such as the laws of conservation of energy and momentum. These laws apply to macroscopic, atomic, as well as to nuclear systems, and they are frequently invoked in solving problems related to such systems, as they were in the case of the Compton effect. These are some of the reasons why, if pressed to defend propositions that are not themselves laws, laws are frequently cited.

Let me turn now to the second question raised at the beginning of this section. Do laws, when cited in explanations, help make possible the satisfaction of the criteria of evaluation discussed in chapter IV? Does the fact that a law is invoked in explaining $q$, i.e. in answering a question $Q$, make or tend to make the answer relevant, correct, deep, complete, unified, and well-organized? It depends on the law and on the question. Even if a law is relevant it may not provide the most accurate answer to a particular question. Galileo's law provides a relevant though not a highly accurate answer to the question 'How does a body fall if dropped in mid air?' Laws of thermodynamics can be used to provide relevant and correct answers to many questions, but deeper answers are supplied by statistical mechanics. Admittedly, saying that an oar partially immersed in water appears bent at the angle it does because light is refracted is not to supply as complete an answer as saying that, according to Snell's law, light when entering a medium of different density is refracted in such a way that the angles of incidence and refraction are related by the formula $\sin i / \sin r = \text{const.}$ On the other hand, in answer to a question regarding free fall, saying, following Galileo's law, that the distance $y$ a body falls depends on the square of the time $t$ and is given by the relationship $y = \frac{1}{2}gt^2$ is not to provide an answer as complete (or accurate) as one in which a formula is cited that includes also a term representing air resistance, e.g. $y = \frac{1}{2}gt^2 - \frac{1}{6}gkt^3$, but is not generally classified as a law. Even if the citing of a given law would provide an answer that is more accurate, complete, and deeper than one in which no law is cited, the situation in question may not call for that degree of accuracy, completeness, or depth.

Certainly with respect to any law there will be some questions for which it provides satisfactory answers. More important, such questions often occur in science, and some of the ways laws function to produce satisfactory explanations in these cases were discussed in earlier sections. My general conclusion, then, is that whether a law is required to make an explanation satisfactory, and whether if cited it will improve the quality of an explanation, depends on the law, on the questions raised, and on the situation. A scientific explanation may or may not require a law, it may or may not be improved by one.

## 4. The Deductive-Nomological Model of Explanation

No theory of explanation has received so much attention as this, and no account of the role of laws in explanations can be complete without comment on it. Of particular interest here is the question of whether general statements, even if they are not laws in our sense, must be part of an explanation. This and other issues concerning the Deductive-Nomological (D-N) model will now be discussed. I cannot hope to do justice to all the arguments pro and con that can be found in the literature. I shall concentrate on a few of the main issues involved, particularly as they relate to my own position on explanation.

Those who espouse this model claim to provide conditions for satisfactory explanations in science. They are not supplying conditions for explanation generally, i.e. ones that hold for explanations whether or not they are satisfactory, nor for satisfactory explanations outside science. Moreover, they do not claim that satisfactory explanations in science always conform to the D-N model; there is also a statistical model which is supposed to be satisfied by many scientific explanations. My discussion, however, will concentrate on the D-N model. I shall consider this model as applied to explanations of particular events, since proponents of the model have not sufficiently developed their ideas for other cases.

A D-N explanation consists of an explanans, which contains statements describing 'initial conditions' and statements describing general facts, and an explanandum, which is a statement describing the event to be explained that is deductively implied by the explanans. (In the statistical model it is required only that the explanans make the explanandum probable without deductively implying it.) For the explanation to be satisfactory the statements of the explanans must be true, in which case we speak of a 'true explanation', or well-confirmed by all the evidence available, in which case we speak of a 'well-confirmed explanation'. The general statements in the explanans are called 'laws' by proponents of the D-N model. They are universal in form (they begin with a universal term like 'All'), and they are not logically equivalent to a finite conjunction of statements mentioning particular items. Proponents of the D-N model admit that they have difficulty expressing other conditions such general statements should satisfy, but they clearly have in mind a much wider class of statements than those classified as laws in science. For example, their general statements include 'All crows are black' and 'All copper melts at 1,083 °C.'. Hereafter I shall use the term 'laws' in quotation marks when referring to such statements.

That the explanans contains 'laws', that it is true or well-confirmed, and that it deductively implies the explanandum, are conditions imposed by this model. Can they be construed as necessary and sufficient conditions? What clouds the issue is the absence of a consideration of contextual matters. Are D-N theorists claiming that in all situations in which an explanation is offered the above conditions (or those of the statistical model) must be satisfied for the explanation to be scientifically acceptable? And are they claiming that in any situation, if the statements formulated satisfy the conditions, they constitute a satisfactory scientific explanation? This is how the D-N theorists are most often interpreted. In my discussion of the model I shall argue that there are sets of statements satisfying the criteria of the D-N model that could not be classified as satisfactory explanations in any situation. I shall also argue that there are explanations that, in many situations, can be deemed perfectly satisfactory scientifically speaking, even though they fail to satisfy the D-N conditions or those of the companion statistical model.

As for my first claim, consider the case of a physician with years of training and experience who examines a patient and declares he will die within twenty-four hours. Let us suppose it is true that whenever a physician with that many years of training and experience examines a patient and declares he will die within twenty-four hours then the patient does in fact die within twenty-four hours. This statement is universal in form and is not logically equivalent to a finite conjunction of statements about particulars; it is a 'law' in the D-N sense. If it is true, as we are supposing, and if it is true that the physician in question has examined the patient and made his declaration then it follows deductively that the patient will die within twenty-four hours. When the patient dies we can construct the following argument:

*C*: At time *t* physician *P* examined the patient and declared that he would be dead within the period *t*+24. Physician *P* has many years of training and experience.

*L*: Whenever a physician with many years of training and experience examines a patient and declares he will be dead within some time span the patient does die within that time span.

*E*: The patient died within the time span *t*+24.

This argument satisfies the D-N requirements for being a satisfactory explanation of the event described in *E*. The explanans contains a 'law' which is true and together with a true statement describing particulars deductively implies the explanandum. If the D-N requirements are construed as providing sufficient conditions for a satisfactory explanation, then any set of statements satisfying them should constitute a satisfactory explanation, no matter what other assumptions we make, at least if these are compatible with those in the D-N explanation. Let us, then, assume that the death of the patient in question was in no way brought on by the examination or prediction of the physician, an assumption that is perfectly compatible with statements *C*, *L*, and *E* of the argument above, and indeed could have been incorporated into the argument itself. Given this assumption, I should claim that in no situation could this argument be regarded as providing a satisfactory explanation of why the patient died, or of why he died within a certain twenty-four-hour period. In no situation would it be satisfactory to explain this event by saying that it was predicted by an expert physician who examined the patient. It is simply untrue that the patient died because an expert physician examined him and said that he would die—even if experts are always correct—unless somehow the physician's examination or his prediction was causally involved in bringing about the death. The argument formulated above does state certain facts which if they were known— as in this case they were—prior to the occurrence of the event would have provided a reasonable basis for believing the event would occur. But what this example shows is that not all such facts, even when they include a 'law', constitute a satisfactory explanation of the event. The D-N theorist equates the concept of satisfactorily explaining an event with providing facts, including some general ones, on the basis of which the event could have been inferred. The example shows that this equation is not always legitimate and that there are cases that satisfy the conditions of the D-N model but in no situation could reasonably be held to be satisfactory explanations.

H

If the D-N requirements do not supply sufficient conditions for satisfactory explanations do they supply necessary ones? To begin with, they do not supply conditions that must be satisfied in all situations in which scientific explanations are given. There are situations in which deducibility of the explanandum from the explanans is not required. It may be perfectly satisfactory to explain why a particular oar partially immersed in water looks bent to cite the fact that according to Snell's law light rays are bent when they travel from one medium to another, e.g. from air to water, even though this does not deductively imply that the oar looks bent. Again, in some situations, it may be perfectly satisfactory to explain an event without invoking any general statements at all. The physicist may explain why a certain track was produced in the cloud chamber by saying that an alpha particle passed through the chamber. These explanations may be perfectly satisfactory, since with respect to the questions being raised they may supply answers that can be regarded as correct and that meet other standards appropriate for the situation. We explain that the oar looks bent because light rays are being bent, and that there is a track in the cloud chamber because an alpha particle has just passed through. These statements are correct, and given the knowledge and concerns of those in $S$, they may provide an appropriate level of understanding.[1]

All this the D-N theorist might grant, but, he will say, if the explanations were completely formulated then the D-N requirements would be satisfied. Of course, in a particular situation $S$ when a general statement is obvious it may not actually be cited. What is cited may be only some particular facts those in $S$ may not know, statements describing which may not deductively imply the explanandum. But if all the facts which are implicitly understood in $S$ were explicitly stated then these statements would contain general truths and together with the statements that are actually cited would deductively imply the explanandum. Otherwise the explanation is incomplete.

The problem with this reply is that whether an explanation can be judged to be complete depends in part on the knowledge and concerns

---

[1] Points of this sort are frequently made by critics of the D-N model. See, e.g. S. F. Barker, 'The Role of Simplicity in Explanation', *Current Issues in the Philosophy of Science*, ed. H. Feigl and G. Maxwell (New York, 1961), 265–74; M. Scriven, 'Explanations, Predictions, and Laws', *Minnesota Studies in the Philosophy of Science*, ed. H. Feigl and G. Maxwell (Minneapolis, 1962) iii. 170–230.

of those in the situation in which it is given. In order to provide an answer to $Q$ the explainer may need to provide answers to questions related to $Q$, and the completeness of his explanation will be determined in part by the extent to which it does this.[1] But what questions these are depends on the situation. Completeness is not something that can be judged solely by examining the explanation and the $Q$. This is not to deny that there are numerous scientific explanations in which 'laws' (even laws) are invoked and in which these, together possibly with other propositions, deductively entail a proposition to be explained. We saw two examples of this earlier in the explanations of the parabolic paths of projectiles and of the Compton effect. However, whether a 'law' and a deductive relationship between explanans and explanandum are required to complete an explanation depends on whether, without these, answers are not provided to questions that are or might be raised by those in $S$ who do not understand $q$. There is no such thing as a complete explanation that will answer all questions pertaining to $q$ that might be raised in all situations by those who fail to understand $q$. What the D-N theorist needs to show is that in any situation if those in that situation do not know or are not given 'laws' which, together with the propositions that are cited, deductively imply the explanandum (or at least provide strong inductive support, in the statistical model), then the explanation is incomplete. Does the D-N theorist have arguments to show this?

One is provided by Hempel who formulates

> ... a general *condition of adequacy for any rationally acceptable explanation of a particular event*. That condition is the following: Any rationally acceptable answer to the question 'Why did event $X$ occur?' must offer information which shows that $X$ was to be expected—if not definitely, as in the case of D-N explanation, then at least with reasonable probability. Thus, the explanatory information must provide good grounds for believing that $X$ did in fact occur; otherwise, that information would give us no adequate reason for saying: 'That explains it—that does show why $X$ occurred.'[2]

Hempel agrees that his condition of adequacy is not *sufficient* for a rationally acceptable explanation, since he also believes that 'laws' must be invoked in showing that $X$ was to be expected. But the above condition of adequacy is meant to explain why a deductive or at least a strong inductive relationship between explanans and explanandum is required. Otherwise the explanans would not be capable of showing that $X$ was to be expected.

[1] Cf. Scriven, op. cit., p. 202.
[2] C. G. Hempel, *Aspects of Scientific Explanation*, pp. 367–8.

I find Hempel's claims here unconvincing. For one thing, he offers no argument in favour of his condition of adequacy. Essentially all he does is state it and restate it. For another, something which satisfies it together with the further condition that a 'law' be cited is by no means guaranteed to be a rationally acceptable explanation in any situation. Recall the earlier physician example in which a 'law' is cited and in which the explanans given does provide good grounds for believing that the patient died when he did, although under no circumstances would it be an acceptable explanation of this. Satisfactorily explaining an event and showing that the event was to be expected are not always the same, even when in the latter case 'laws' are invoked.

Most importantly, the condition that a satisfactory explanation of an event must provide good grounds for believing it did occur is too strong. Hempel readily admits that 'it is not, of course, the *purpose* of an explanation to provide grounds in support of the explanandum-statement'.[1] But, he adds, 'an adequate explanation cannot help providing information which, if properly established, also provides grounds in support of the explanandum-statement'.[2] What, then, is the purpose of an explanation, or, to put the question in a better way, what is one's purpose in offering an explanation to those in a given situation? One might have a number of purposes, but, in considering the position stated in chapter IV, we might also speak of the main intellectual purpose. In this sense one's purpose in citing $E$, within situation $S$, as providing an explanation of $q$ is to provide what one believes is or might be a correct answer to $Q$ in order to enable those in $S$ to understand $q$.[3] If so then Hempel is certainly right that it is not, or at least need not be, part of the main intellectual purpose of an explanation of an event to provide good grounds for believing that it occurred. The important question is whether in order to achieve the main intellectual purpose of an explanation one does as a matter of fact have to provide such grounds. To be sure, if I assert that $E$ explains $q$, where $q$ is 'why some event occurred', then I am committed to the claim that the event did in fact occur. But this is not Hempel's point. Hempel is claiming that if $E$ explains $q$ then $E$, considered by itself, should provide good grounds for believing that the event described in $q$ occurred. So the question we must ask is this: In order to enable those in a situation $S$ to understand why a certain event occurred must the answer that is supplied provide good grounds for believing that it did occur?

[1] Ibid., p. 368.    [2] Ibid.    [3] See chapter IV, section 1.

This question is answered in the negative by many opponents of the D-N model. They present numerous counter-examples, and I shall cite one supplied by Arthur Collins.[1] A small percentage of those injected with penicillin develop a rash, for the sake of argument, say 2 per cent. Suppose Jones develops a rash. What is the explanation? It is that he was injected with penicillin. Now even though the fact that Jones was injected with penicillin does not by itself provide good grounds for believing that Jones got a rash—because only 2 per cent of those so injected do—nevertheless this fact could be cited, in a given situation *S*, to enable those in *S* to understand why the rash occurred. The proposition 'Jones was injected with penicillin' provides a correct answer to the question 'Why did Jones get a rash?'.

Hempel replies to such counter-examples by denying that they provide satisfactory explanations. 'Surely the mere information that the patient had [a penicillin injection] does not suffice to explain his [rash], precisely because in most cases [penicillin injections do not produce rashes].'[2] What we need to know, Hempel would probably say, is why Jones got a rash when 98 per cent of those who take penicillin do not. Jones must have some physiological condition which, in conjunction with the penicillin, produces the rash, and it is this fact, together with the 'law' that all (or almost all) people in that condition who take penicillin get a rash, that must be cited in an adequate explanation. In this reply, what has been done is to shift the question and the situation for which the original explanation is designed. The question has been shifted from 'Why did Jones get a rash?' to 'Why did Jones, who took penicillin, get a rash, when 98 per cent of those who take penicillin do not?' The situation for which the original explanation was designed has been shifted from one in which someone, e.g. a physician, wants to know what particular event precipitated the occurrence of the rash, whether it was some injection Jones had, something he ate, the heat, or what, to one in which someone wants to know what sort of physiological condition Jones is in that allows something like a penicillin injection to produce a rash. Given the former situation the proposition 'Jones received a penicillin injection' can provide an answer to the question 'Why did Jones get a rash?' that is correct and that satisfies criteria of completeness and

[1] A. Collins, 'The Use of Statistics in Explanation', *British Journal for the Philosophy of Science*, 17 (1966), 127–40.

[2] *Aspects of Scientific Explanation*, p. 369. Hempel is here discussing a similar counter-example proposed by Stephen Barker, op. cit., regarding pneumonia causing death.

depth *appropriate for that situation*. Given the second situation such an answer would, of course, be inadequate. The criteria appropriate for the former situation are satisfied even though the explanans does not provide good grounds for believing that the event described in the explanandum occurred. I conclude that Hempel's reply does not establish that satisfactorily explaining an event always requires supplying good grounds for believing that it occurred.

Let me turn now to the claim that a satisfactory explanation must contain general statements or 'laws'. Why do proponents of the D-N model believe this? Basically, I think, for two reasons. First, they hold that an explanation which contains no 'laws' must itself be justified by appeal to 'laws'. If the occurrence of a particular event $e_1$ is cited as the explanation of event $e_2$, then in justifying the claim that this explanation is correct one would need to invoke some general 'law' that relates events of type $e_1$ to events of type $e_2$, the simplest example of which would be 'If an event of type $e_1$ occurs then an event of type $e_2$ occurs'.

This reason is by no means compelling. For one thing, in presenting an explanation in a situation $S$, the explainer may justify what he says in many ways, depending on the sort of challenge that is or might be made by those in $S$. The challenge need not always require a justification by appeal to 'laws'. One may justify one's claim that the penicillin injection explains Jones's rash by providing evidence that Jones did indeed take penicillin and did not eat any rash-producing foods, was not exposed to high temperatures, did not come in contact with poison ivy, and so on. One justifies an explanatory claim by meeting certain actual and possible challenges that are particularly appropriate in the circumstances, not all possible challenges, something obviously impossible. The challenges that are appropriate to meet in a given situation do not necessarily call for the citing of 'laws'. Moreover, even if a 'law' is invoked in meeting a challenge it does not follow that it must be considered, in any reasonable sense, a part of the original explanation; any more than the evidence suggesting that Jones did take penicillin—e.g. the fact that after the injection was given the doctor wrote down on Jones's chart that an injection was given—need be considered a part of the explanation of why Jones got a rash.[1] Admittedly, there are situations in which appropriate

---

[1] Michael Scriven, possibly the staunchest critic of the D-N model, was one of the first to note the latter's refusal to distinguish explanations from what he calls 'grounds' for explanations. See, e.g., his 'Explanations, Predictions, and

challenges call for the formulation of general statements. What cannot be said is that this is so for all situations or that when 'laws' are invoked to defend an explanation they must always be considered part of the explanation itself.

The second reason for the claim that a satisfactory explanation must contain 'laws' has to do with the meaning of an explanatory statement. Suppose it is claimed that $E$ explains $q$, where $q$ is 'why some event occurred' and $E$ contains reference to some other event but no 'laws'. It is an implication of such a claim, the D-N theorist may say, that any event sufficiently similar to that referred to in $q$ can also be explained by the citing of an event sufficiently similar to that referred to in $E$. For example, if it is claimed that Jones's penicillin injection explains the occurrence of his rash then it follows that any rash sufficiently similar to Jones's could also be explained by citing an event sufficiently similar to Jones's penicillin injection. But the latter statement is a general truth or 'law' implied by an explanatory claim and so a part of that claim. Hence 'laws' are parts of explanations.

There is a kernel of truth in this, but much else besides. What is right is the idea that the following statement would be logically odd: 'Jones had a penicillin injection and got a rash because of it; Smith also got a rash after being injected with penicillin but not because of the injection; and no relevant difference exists between the two men or the situations in which they were injected that could be cited in correctly explaining why one got a rash because of the injection and the other did not.' The general point is that if you claim that a certain event of type $E$ can be correctly explained by citing a certain event of type $E'$, then if events of the same type recur and you claim that one event cannot be correctly explained by citing the other, you must be prepared to allow that there are relevant differences between the events or the situations in which they occurred that can be appealed to in correctly explaining why in the one case, but not the other, an event of type $E$ can be correctly explained by citing an event of type $E'$. This, I believe, is the kernel of truth in the generality claim. But notice three things. First, this statement, though general, is very indefinite. It says nothing about the respects in which the events or situations are relevantly similar or dissimilar. Second, it is really a comment on the concept of explanation or correct explanation, rather

Laws', pp. 196 ff.; also I. Scheffler, *The Anatomy of Inquiry* (New York, 1963), p. 39.

than anything worthy of being called a law, even in the D-N theorist's sense of 'law'. It is not a general truth about events in the world, but about what is involved in a claim that something is a correct explanation of an event. Third, this general truth could in no reasonable sense be said to be a part of an explanation itself. If I claim that the penicillin injection correctly explains Jones's rash it is not a part of my explanation of Jones's rash that I am prepared to give the same explanation when someone else gets a rash after a penicillin injection unless I am also prepared to maintain the existence of relevant differences between the cases.

A final matter to be noted concerns the contextual nature of explanation. D-N theorists on occasion pay lip-service to the idea that explanations are given by people in situations for certain purposes, but they propose to isolate what they call the 'logical' features of explanation from what they call the 'pragmatic' features. The D-N model describes features of the former sort not the latter. It seems to be part of this view that although there are contextual aspects of an explanation, a group of statements can be judged to be a satisfactory explanation, from a scientific point of view, without considering these. By contrast, the account of explanation I have proposed holds that independently of contextual considerations it is not possible to classify a set of statements as an explanation, let alone to determine whether it is a satisfactory one. Suppose we discover the following statements scrawled on a sheet of paper: 'All men are mortal. Socrates is a man. Therefore, Socrates is mortal.' Is this an explanation? If the D-N requirements noted earlier are sufficient the answer must be Yes, since it contains a true 'law' which, together with a second true statement, deductively implies the third statement. My position is that whether it can be classified as an explanation depends on the context of classification in which is considered the type of person who did or might cite the first two statements in attempting to render understandable Socrates' mortality and the type of situation in which he might do so. If these matters are not determined then the question of whether to classify this as an explanation, as opposed, say, to an exercise in logic or just idle doodling, has no answer. Moreover, these matters need to be determined to decide whether, if it is an explanation, it is a good one, since to evaluate an explanation, inside as well as outside science, one must consider the sorts of questions raised, the concerns of those raising them, and their knowledge and beliefs.

My conclusions regarding the D-N model of explanation are these.

Neither general statements nor a deductive relationship between explanans and explanandum are always required for an explanation in science to be satisfactory. Certainly they are not sufficient, even when other conditions stipulated by D-N theorists are added. This can be determined by appeal to counter-examples as well as to the contextual nature of explanation. Both general statements and a deductive relationship may be required if the situation in which the explanation is given or the questions that are being raised require it; but they may not, even in justifying the answers that are given. To be sure, explanation is, in a sense, general. But the sense in which it is does not warrant the claim that within every satisfactory explanation in science there lurks a general statement about events in the world.

## 5. Conclusions

I have been dealing with the issue of the roles laws play in providing explanations. In the first section, by appeal to various characteristics of laws, I indicated some of the ways laws can provide explanations by answering questions pertaining to one or more of these characteristics. Depending on the question that is raised and the situation, a law may provide an explanation in virtue of some theoretical idea it contains, the factors it isolates, the manner in which it relates these factors, or any combination of these. The explanation of the Compton effect was cited in section 2 to illustrate a typical use of laws in scientific explanation. By introducing certain quantum ideas Compton restructured the scattering problem as an elastic-collision problem, to which the laws of conservation of energy and momentum could then be applied and an equation describing the effect derived. In section 3 the issue was whether laws are required for, or at least improve the quality of, scientific explanations, and the answer was that this depends on the question and situation. Finally, in section 4 the Deductive-Nomological model of explanation was examined according to which general statements, even if they are not laws in science, must be part of an explanation. I argued that this is not so, and furthermore that the model fails to provide either necessary or sufficient conditions for satisfactory explanations in science.

# VI. Some Modes of Reasoning

One question that can be raised in the study of a law is how the scientist arrived at it and what he did with it once it was formulated. This is not simply of historical interest, since there are philosophical issues pertaining to the nature of the scientist's reasoning. It is with these that the present chapter is concerned. I shall consider various answers to the question of what sort of reasoning is involved when a law is proposed and I shall also attempt to formulate some general modes of reasoning. In the latter instance my aim is a restricted one. I shall not discuss problems such as the justification of induction or the possibility of formalizing and quantifying modes of reasoning. My aim simply is to set forth a number of modes of reasoning that seem appropriate for scientific laws, to examine some philosophical views that pertain to their use, and to do these things in such a way that, in chapter VII, it will be possible to discuss the extent to which these modes are employed in actual scientific reasoning when laws are proposed.

## 1. The Hypothetico-Deductive View

On this view the scientist begins with a problem in the light of which a hypothesis—in this case a law—is formulated. Consequences are derived deductively from the law, possibly in conjunction with other assumptions, and are subjected to empirical tests. Among those who defend this view is Karl Popper. A law, according to Popper, is not arrived at by inference from observations. Statements describing what has been observed cannot deductively imply a law, since the latter is general in a way that the former are not. And Popper rejects the idea of an inductive inference from the data to the law. Observation statements cannot provide a basis from which to infer laws, they provide a basis only for testing them. When a law is proposed its deductive consequences are tested by seeing whether they are compatible with the observation statements. If they are not the law is refuted. How the scientist arrives at the law in the first place is an empirical question which the psychologist might be able to answer. There may be a causal explanation of how the scientist came to have his ideas, but there is no inference involved *to* the law, only *from* it. Popper speaks of theories, including laws, as *'free* creations of our own minds, the result of an almost poetic intuition'.[1]

Others who defend the hypothetico-deductive view speak in similar ways. Hempel writes:

> The transition from data to theory requires creative imagination. Scientific hypotheses are not derived from observed facts, but invented in order to account for them. They constitute guesses at the connections that might obtain between the phenomena under study, at uniformities and patterns that might underlie their occurrence.[2]

The view is a popular one among scientists. Here is how the physicist Feynman expresses it:

> In general we look for a new law by the following process. First we guess it. Then we compute the consequences of the guess to see what would be implied if this law that we guessed is right. Then we compare the result of the computation to nature, with experiment or experience, compare it directly with observation, to see if it works. If it disagrees with experiment it is wrong. In that simple statement is the key to science.[3]

Some proponents of this view recognize, however, that certain laws are logical consequences of others; e.g. the law of conservation of linear momentum follows deductively from Newton's laws of motion, which do not follow from anything more fundamental. Accordingly, a distinction is sometimes made between *fundamental* and *derived* laws. Fundamental laws are not derived from any others, but are products of 'scientific imagination' and 'poetic intuition'. Derived laws are logical consequences of fundamental ones together possibly with other assumptions.

According to the hypothetico-deductive view scientists do not make inferences to (fundamental) laws, only from them. How should this claim be construed? One way would be to say that the term 'inference' is being used in a restricted sense to cover only deductive inferences from statements describing particular observations. On this construction the hypothetico-deductive theorists would be saying simply that scientists do not make deductive inferences to laws from non-general

[1] K. Popper, *Conjectures and Refutations* (London, 1965), p. 192.
[2] C. G. Hempel, *Philosophy of Natural Science* (Englewood Cliffs, N.J., 1966), p. 15.
[3] R. Feynman, *The Character of Physical Law* (Cambridge, Mass., 1967), p. 156.

observation statements. The problem with this construction is that it does not do full justice to the claims of the hypothetico-deductive theorist. First, proponents of this view also deny that scientists arrive at hypotheses via inductive inferences. Popper, e.g., writes that 'induction, i.e. inference based on many observations, is a myth. It is neither a psychological fact, nor a fact of ordinary life, nor one of scientific procedure.'[1] He holds that scientists and others do not in fact employ inductive inferences and that in principle they could not justifiably do so, since inductive reasoning is fallacious. While other hypothetico-deductivists do not accept Popper's view about the fallacy of inductive reasoning, they do share his view that as a matter of fact scientists do not arrive at hypotheses via this mode of reasoning. Second, by saying that scientific hypotheses are invented, guessed, free creations of our own minds, hypothetico-deductivists appear to be contrasting these cases with those involving inferences. The claim seems to be that the scientist arrives at a law not by making an inference, not by engaging in a process of reasoning in which something is concluded on the basis of something else, but by making a conjecture. This conjecture may be a causal consequence of observations (among other things) but it is not inferred from them. Only after the conjecture is made do inferences occur.

To examine this view something must first be said about the concept of inference. What do we mean when we speak of a person as having inferred something? There are, I believe, two slightly different uses of 'infer'. In one use, when we say that $A$ inferred that a proposition $p$ is true or probable from the fact, or alleged fact, that $q$ is true, we imply that $A$ came to believe that $p$ is true or probable. In another use, we imply simply that $A$ believed that $p$ is true or probable. In both uses we also imply that when $A$ came to believe (believed) that $p$ is true or probable his reason for believing this was the fact, or alleged fact, that $q$ is true.[2] (If we know $q$ to be false, we will say that $A$'s reason for believing that $p$ is true or probable was his *belief* that $q$ is true.) But more must be involved in his reason than this. Suppose $A$ comes to believe that God exists, and that when he does so his reason for believing this is the alleged fact $q$, that if God does exist and he does not believe it then God will punish him. Although $A$ has

[1] Popper, op. cit., p. 53.

[2] For a theory of inference according to which the second use of 'infer' is basic and the first is derivative, see D. G. Brown, 'The Nature of Inference', *Philosophical Review*, 64 (1955), 351–69.

come to believe that God exists and $A$'s reason for believing this is the alleged fact that $q$ is true, $A$ has not *inferred* that God exists from this alleged fact. He has not done so because the alleged fact which constitutes $A$'s reason for believing that God exists is not a fact which $A$ believes makes it likely that God exists. It is, as we might say, a pragmatic or utilitarian reason rather than an 'evidential' one, and it is only reasons of the latter sort that are involved in inferences. Accordingly, in what follows when I speak of $A$'s reason for a certain belief I shall mean his 'evidential' reason. However, if we want to spell out the conditions under which it is appropriate to say that $A$ inferred that $p$ is true or probable from the fact, or alleged fact, that $q$ is true they are these:

1. $A$ came to believe (or believed) that $p$ is true or probable.
2. When $A$ did so his reason for believing this was the fact, or alleged fact, that $q$ is true and the fact, or alleged fact, that $q$'s being true makes it likely that $p$ is true.

Reasoning is a broader concept. It includes, among other things, thinking about something and drawing certain conclusions, which means thinking leading to an inference (in either sense); it also includes examining a reason to see if it does support a belief. Hypothetico-deductivists do not deny that there is reasoning in the case of laws. They simply assert that it is all of the second type: It involves only the examination of reasons to see if they do support a law, and so it takes place after the law is formulated. Their claim is that there is no reasoning which leads to laws in the first place; scientists do not infer laws, in the coming-to-believe sense of 'infer' (which is the one that will be used in what follows).[1] It is this view that I want to reject.

In the early years of the nineteenth century Gay-Lussac performed experiments in which gases were combined to form new compounds. In his experiments he noted, e.g., that 100 parts (by volume) of oxygen combine with 200 parts of hydrogen to form water and that 100 parts of muriatic gas combine with 100 parts of ammonia gas to form ammonium chloride. After considering several other cases he wrote: 'Thus it appears evident to me that gases always combine in the simplest proportions when they act on one another.' (This is essentially Gay-Lussac's law.) Gay-Lussac came to believe that gases combine in simple ratios and when he did so his reason for believing

---

[1] Those who, following Brown, think that the second sense of 'infer' is basic can understand the thesis under examination as saying that scientists do not *come to infer* laws from data. See Brown, op. cit., p. 355.

this was the fact that various gases he observed combine in simple ratios. From his experiments he inferred that gases behave in this way. It may be objected that Gay-Lussac in writing the words he did was not describing how he really came to believe the law. Quite possibly the law occurred to him after considering a single experiment with oxygen and hydrogen. It might also be objected that the law did not occur to Gay-Lussac simply on the basis of experimentation; a background in atomic theory was relevant as well. Let us grant that theoretical ideas played a part in the origin of Gay-Lussac's law. (I will go into this in the next chapter.) Still there is an inference involved. It may be an inference from the result of one experiment together with theoretical assumptions. And the conclusion might not be the strong one that the law is definitely true, but a weaker one to the effect that the law *may* be true. Nevertheless, on the basis of at least certain experiments and theoretical assumptions Gay-Lussac came to believe that (there is some likelihood that) gases combine in simple ratios by volume.

Why do proponents of the hypothetico-deductive account deny the existence of inferences to laws? There seem to be several strands in their thinking. First, they hold that there is no mechanical way to infer laws from data. As Hempel puts it, 'There are . . . no generally applicable "rules of induction" by which hypotheses can be mechanically derived or inferred from empirical data.'[1] Second, they hold that laws and hypotheses generally are arrived at by an act of imagination. Third, they hold that a law is not inferable from a set of empirical data alone; no such set will yield a law. Fourth, they hold that the formulation of a hypothesis on the part of the scientist is a causal process in which many things are involved in addition to the observations he has made and the theories he holds, e.g. his personality, his training, and even his dreams.

We can grant these facts, but none of them establishes the non-existence of inferences to laws. First, from the fact that laws cannot be inferred by mechanical reasoning from data it does not follow that they cannot be inferred. We might speak of someone as having engaged in mechanical reasoning leading to an inference from *q* to *p* if there are rules that permit *p* to be correctly inferred from *q* (rules that indicate that having *q* as a reason for believing *p* when one comes to believe it is legitimate), if there are rules prescribing how the reasoning shall proceed (through what steps, or, if there are several

[1] Hempel, op. cit., p. 15.

possible ways, through what alternations of steps), and if the person actually came to believe *p* for which he had reason *q* solely by a conscious application of these rules. Given this characterization, it should be obvious that scientists do not engage in mechanical reasoning to laws. They do not infer laws from data solely by a conscious application of rules of the sort referred to above. But it does not follow from this that they make no inferences to laws. A scientist may make an inference from data to law without engaging in reasoning that consists simply in a conscious application of rules that indicate what follows from what and what steps to take. Second, from the fact that to arrive at a law requires 'creative imagination' or 'poetic intuition' it does not follow that laws cannot be inferred. We might say that someone's inference involved imagination if the reasoning that led to it was not mechanical in the sense noted above. Many inferences that are made involve imagination; they are not mechanical but they are inferences none the less.

Third, it may be the case that a law is not inferable from a set of empirical data alone, since background information will also be relevant. But this would not preclude an inference to the law from the data, in the light of background information. It does not preclude coming to believe the law where one's reason for believing it is that the data and background information are what they are. Fourth, a scientist might not have made an inference from data to hypothesis if he had not had the personality, training, and dreams that he did have. He made the inference none the less, and the fact that he did make this particular inference instead of some other or none at all might be causally explained, in part at least, by reference to his personality, training, and dreams. The fact that there is a causal explanation of how a scientist came to have a certain reason for believing a law or of why he believed it for that reason (what in his personality, training, or other circumstances allowed him to believe it for that reason) does not preclude his having come to believe that law and having that reason for believing it. It does not preclude his having made an inference to the law from observation and theory. Finally, there is no necessary incompatibility between conjecture and inference. A scientist may have made an inference to a hypothesis on the basis of data and the hypothesis may still be a conjecture, depending upon how strongly the data support the hypothesis.

Earlier I considered and rejected the idea that hypothetico-deductivists are using the term 'inference' in a restricted sense to cover only deductive inferences from observation statements. It might now be said that what the theorists in question mean by inferring *p* from *q* is generating *p* from *q* mechanically in accordance with a set of rules. The analogy would be with adding a column of numbers, in which the answer is generated by applying a set of arithmetic rules. This view simply equates reasoning with mechanical reasoning, as characterized above. If so then perhaps charity demands that we construe the hypothetico-deductive thesis simply as the claim that scientists do not engage in mechanical reasoning to laws. And since we have agreed that this is right, there is no point in objecting to the theory, except perhaps to complain of lack of clarity in its presentation.

However, it is by no means evident that its defenders want to make this their sole claim. For one thing, there is also no mechanical reasoning *from* laws once they are formulated. Scientists do not infer conclusions from laws in a mechanical manner. Accordingly, if hypothetico-deductivists are equating reasoning with mechanical reasoning, then they would have to preclude not only inferences to laws but inferences from them as well. More importantly, it is also their view that cognitive activities of the scientist during the course of which a hypothesis is formed are not subject to philosophical scrutiny. The discovery of a law is essentially a non-rational affair involving 'creative imagination' and flashes of insight, which are capable only of psychological investigation. To say this, however, is to preclude without justification an important part of the scientist's activity that is subject to philosophical analysis. It is to preclude an analysis of the sorts of reasons scientists have for laws when they come to believe them. It is to preclude (non-mechanical) inferences scientists make that can be described from a philosophical point of view.

What must now be determined is what sorts of inferences are involved in the case of laws. This means characterizing the various types of reasons that scientists have for laws when they come to believe them and expressing these as 'modes of inference'. The latter will also indicate the kinds of reasons which scientists can offer in support of a law which they already believe and hence are not inferring. (Accordingly, when I speak of 'modes of inference' I do not thereby imply that one who has or gives reasons that are in conformity with these modes is necessarily making an inference. He may be, but he may also be in the position of having or giving reasons for something that he or someone else has already inferred.)

## 2. Retroduction

No philosopher has been so sharply critical of the hypothetico-deductive view as N. R. Hanson. He argues that scientists do make inferences to laws, and that the most important are neither deductive nor inductive ones. How, e.g., did Kepler arrive at his first law regarding the orbit of the planets?

> Kepler did not *begin* with the hypothesis that mars' orbit was elliptical and then deduce statements confirmed by Brahe's observations. These latter observations were given, and they set the problem—they were Johannes Kepler's starting point. He struggled back from these, first to one hypothesis, then to another, then to another, and ultimately to the hypothesis of the elliptical orbit.[1]

This struggle involved a form of inference that is not deductive or inductive, but what Hanson, borrowing a term from Peirce, calls 'retroductive'. The scientist begins by considering puzzling phenomena that have been observed. He makes an inference to a hypothesis which, if true, would explain the phenomena by organizing them into an 'intelligible, systematic, conceptual pattern'. Hanson characterizes the retroductive mode of inference as follows:

> Some surprising phenomenon *P* is observed.
> *P* would be explicable as a matter of course if *H* were true.
> Hence there is reason to think that *H* is true.[2]

Peirce held essentially the same viewpoint:

> Every inquiry whatsoever takes its rise in the observation . . . of some surprising phenomenon. . . . The inquiry begins with pondering these phenomena in all their aspects, in the search of some point of view whence the wonder shall be resolved. At length a conjecture arises that furnishes a possible Explanation, by which I mean a syllogism exhibiting the surprising fact as necessarily consequent upon the circumstances of its occurrence together with the truth of the credible conjecture, as premises. On account of this Explanation, the inquirer is led to regard his conjecture, or hypothesis, with favor. As I phrase it, he provisionally holds it to be 'Plausible'. . . . [The] characteristic formula of reasoning [involved in this process] I term Retroduction, i.e., reasoning from consequent to antecedent.[3]

According to this viewpoint, there is an inference that is made when a law is proposed. This inference is from observed surprising

---

[1] N. R. Hanson, *Patterns of Discovery* (Cambridge, 1958), p. 72.

[2] Ibid., p. 86.

[3] C. S. Peirce, 'A Neglected Argument for the Reality of God', reprinted in part in *Science: Men, Methods, Goals*, ed. B. Brody and N. Capaldi (New York, 1968), pp. 143–9; quotation from pp. 143–4.

phenomena, and from the fact that the law, if true, would explain these phenomena, to the conclusion that there is reason to think that the law is true.

Several problems beset the retroductive account. To begin with, the claim that the scientist always starts by considering simply observed phenomena is unacceptable. Maxwell developed his distribution law for molecular velocities by considering not observed phenomena but the unobserved molecular nature of a gas postulated by kinetic theory. Furthermore, even when the scientist develops a law by considering observed phenomena, this, in the typical case, is not all he considers. Usually a theoretical background is also relevant. Gay-Lussac did not infer his law simply from his experiments with hydrogen and oxygen, but from these together with, or in the light of, a theory he held about the molecular structure of gases and forces between molecules. The retroductive inference, as characterized by Peirce and Hanson, in the passages quoted above, neglects the background of theory that the scientist usually has to begin with which often provides at least part of the basis for an inference to a law.[1]

The main problem, however, is that the retroductive mode of inference, as described above, is fallacious. From the fact that a hypothesis $H$, if true, would explain the data it does not in general follow that there is reason to think that $H$ is true. The hypothesis that I will be paid \$1 million when I complete this book would, if it were true, explain why I am writing the book. But this provides no reason for thinking that I am about to become a millionaire. There are many 'wild' hypotheses which if true would explain the data, but unless there is some other evidence in their favour, this fact by itself lends no plausibility to them.

Hanson and Peirce may reply that when they speak of explanation they mean 'the best explanation', and when they speak of explaining the data they mean explaining the data in the light of all the background information available, i.e. in such a way that the explanation is consonant with this background information. The hypothesis that I will be paid \$1 million when I complete this book would not offer the best explanation of why I am writing it, in the light of everything else that is known—or so it might be said. Let me turn, then, to a

---

[1] Hanson in his work does emphasize the role of theory in organizing and interpreting data, but when he is talking about retroduction he claims that one begins with the empirical data and then develops a theory to organize and interpret those data.

view according to which non-deductive inference always involves inference to the best explanation.

## 3. Inference to the Best Explanation

The retroductive mode of inference has been formulated by Gilbert Harman in a manner that seems to obviate difficulties in Hanson and Peirce. Harman claims that all inductive inference is, in reality, inference to the best explanation. According to Harman, when the detective pondering the evidence concludes that the butler committed the crime he is reasoning that this hypothesis provides the best explanation of the evidence; when we infer that all crows are black we do so because this hypothesis offers the best explanation of the fact that all observed crows are black (better, e.g. than the hypothesis that we have been observing a biased sample). In his first article on this subject Harman stated that induction always infers an explanation of one's evidence.[1] In a later article he gives this up, claiming that what is explained by the hypothesis is not always the evidence.[2] In this later article Harman states that 'in inductive inference one may directly infer by one step of inference only a conclusion of the form *A explains B*'.[3] From this conclusion we may, by deduction, infer *A*. Furthermore, he states, the explanation inferred must be the best of *competing* (i.e. mutually incompatible) explanations and not simply the best of alternative explanations which may not conflict.

Harman speaks of an inference to the conclusion '*A* explains *B*', which I shall rewrite as 'Hypothesis *H* explains facts (events, etc.) *F*'. From what is this conclusion supposed to be inferred, and what is the pattern of inference? Harman does not provide a definite answer, but he does give some clues. To begin with, *H* is supposed to supply the best of competing explanations of *F*, and 'the criteria of the "best" of competing explanations include not only explanatory power but also epistemic considerations; e.g. an inferable explanation must be probable on one's evidence'.[4] This, together with other claims Harman makes, suggests that at least one thing from which an explanation is inferred is the evidence *E* for the hypothesis. But since the explanation of *F* which *H* supplies is considered, as are the explanations offered by competitors, it might be useful to state these

---

[1] G. Harman, 'The Inference to the Best Explanation', *Philosophical Review*, 64 (1965), 88–95.
[2] 'Enumerative Induction as Inference to the Best Explanation', *Journal of Philosophy*, 65 (1968), 529–33.
[3] Ibid., p. 530.                                                        [4] Ibid.

explanations in a separate premise. Also, since the inference is supposed to involve inference to the best explanation, it might be more illuminating to state several conclusions. One is '*H* provides the best of competing explanations of *F*'; another is '*H* explains *F*'; another, which follows from this, is simply *H*. Whether the first conclusion is warranted will depend on its probability in the light of the evidence and on its explanatory power. Accordingly, the present pattern of inference might be stated in the form of an argument, as follows, in which the premisses indicate reasons for believing conclusion 1, which in turn indicates a reason for believing conclusions 2 and 3:

Premiss 1: Evidence *E* is obtained.

Premiss 2: With respect to *F*, hypothesis *H* offers such and such an explanation, whereas competing hypotheses offer such and such other explanations.

Conclusion 1: *H* provides the best of competing explanations of *F*. (Whether this conclusion is warranted depends on its probability in the light of the evidence *E* and on the explanatory power of *H* and its competitors.)

Conclusion 2: *H* explains *F*.

Conclusion 3: *H*.

This form of inference requires clarification as well as modification. One need for improvement is reflected in some points Harman himself goes on to make as well as in one of the difficulties previously mentioned with Hanson's retroductive inference. Typically, an inference is made from the evidence *E in the light of everything else we know or take for granted*, e.g. in the light of accepted theories, principles, laws, and observational data other than *E*. (Harman himself recognizes this when he says that we want our conclusion to fit in with existing knowledge.)[1] Accordingly, the first premiss of the argument could be changed to read: Evidence *E* is obtained in the light of background information *B*. Second, when a scientist reasons about a hypothesis often his conclusion is not that the hypothesis is true or highly probable, but that it is plausible, that there is some probability that it is true, that it is a reasonable hypothesis to consider further. (This, indeed, seems to be the sort of reasoning Hanson and Peirce had in mind, but not Harman since he is concerned only with inductive inferences in which the conclusion is inferred with high probability.) If this is the conclusion then it need not be required that the hypothesis in question provides the *best* of competing explanations.

[1] Ibid., p. 531.

Something weaker can be stated, perhaps that the hypothesis provides an explanation that is as good as, or at least is not markedly inferior to, other competing ones. A scientist may be willing to conclude that *H* has some plausibility, even if he believes that some incompatible *H'* may provide a somewhat better explanation, especially if he is not fully satisfied with the explanation provided by *H'*.

Third, when in fact a hypothesis is judged to offer a plausible explanation the class of hypotheses with which it is being compared does not contain all possible competitors. Comparisons are made with hypotheses that can be deemed reasonable to consider as alternatives given the evidence *E* and background information *B*. Such hypotheses do not comprise a precisely defined class, but might include those that have actually been proposed by respectable scientists aware of *B* or of *B* and *E*, as well as hypotheses that have not but might easily have been proposed by such people. In any case, not even all of these hypotheses, but only some, will usually be explicitly considered by a person *A* who reasons to the plausibility of a hypothesis *H*. In certain cases no competing hypotheses may be explicitly considered. In the former situation *A* infers that *H* provides a good explanation of *F* from the evidence, the fact that *H* provides such and such answers to questions concerning *F*, and the fact that such and such competing hypotheses provide other answers. In the latter case he infers that *H* provides a good explanation of *F* from the evidence and from the fact that *H* provides such and such answers, where he *assumes* that any competing hypotheses that it is reasonable to consider, given *E* and *B*, do not provide much more plausible answers. If this assumption is incorrect then his inference can be criticized. Even in the first case if there are competing hypotheses in addition to the ones *A* actually considers that are reasonable to consider, given *E* and *B*, and if these provide much more plausible answers than *H*, then *A*'s inference is subject to criticism.

Fourth, there is the question of what meaning can be attached to the concept of explanatory power, a notion Harman does not discuss. Referring to my account of explanation in chapter IV, this concept might be related to a number of criteria cited there, e.g. depth, completeness, unification, and simplicity (cited under 'correctness'). Consider various questions pertaining to *F*. We are to imagine that these questions, and the situations in which they are raised, call for answers that provide explanations of *F*. Suppose hypothesis *H* is capable of supplying answers that, given *E*, *B*, and *F*, are unifying, deep, complete, and simple (or that have some of these features). Suppose that no competing hypothesis known by those acquainted with $E$, $B$, and $F$ is capable of offering answers that are as good, on the whole, with respect to the above criteria. If so we can say that $H$ has more 'explanatory power' with respect to $F$ than any of the known competing hypotheses. This fact provides at least some basis for saying that $H$ is plausible.

Fifth, Harman distinguishes 'explanatory power' from 'probability in the light of the evidence', but it is not clear that this can be done. If $H$ is capable of providing answers to questions concerning $F$ and these answers, in the light of the evidence $E$ and background information $B$, are unifying, deep, complete, and simple—i.e. they provide unification for $F$ within the background information and evidence, they provide deep, complete, and simple answers to questions about $F$—then such answers must have some degree of probability on the basis of the evidence. If probability in the light of the evidence is a separate, unrelated criterion, how is it to be determined? We cannot say that the answers provided by $H$ are probable in the light of the evidence if they provide a plausible explanation of $F$, because this is to be a conclusion of the argument. Nor, if the explanatory mode of inference is basic, can we equate probability in the light of the evidence with inductive support by simple enumeration of instances. We shall have to understand 'explanatory power' in such a way that if, given the evidence and background information, $H$ has more explanatory power than its competitors, then it is more probable than its competitors, in the light of the evidence and background information.

Sixth, answers to questions pertaining to $F$ are supplied typically not by a single hypothesis $H$ but by that hypothesis in conjunction with others which form part of the background information. (Some of these auxiliary hypotheses may even need to be modified if $H$ is to be accepted.) It is the answers provided by $H$ together with certain other hypotheses that need to be considered in evaluating explanations. This fact must be expressed in the second premiss of the explanatory mode of inference.

Finally, as emphasized in chapter IV, the goodness of an explanation is to be judged relative to a situation in which it is, or can be, given; the knowledge and concerns of those in such a situation are to be considered. Two (non-conflicting) explanations may be such that one is deeper and provides more unification than the other, but unless we know the situation in which it is to be used we cannot conclude that it is a better explanation. This idea should be expressed as part of the conclusion of an explanatory argument.

With these modifications the explanatory mode of inference can be formulated as follows:

### Explanatory Inference

Premiss 1: Evidence $E$ is obtained in the light of background information $B$. (Or: Facts $E$ are assumed in the light of background information $B$.)

Premiss 2: $H$, possibly in conjunction with certain other assumptions, is capable of providing a set of answers $S$ to questions concerning facts $F$ which may be part of $E$ or $B$. (Incompatible competing hypotheses $H_2,..., H_n$ that it is reasonable to consider, given $E$ and $B$, when conjoined with auxiliary hypotheses are capable of providing sets of answers $S_2,..., S_n$ to questions concerning $F$, or, in some cases, no answers at all.)

Conclusion 1: It is plausible to suppose that $H$, when conjoined with certain other assumptions, is capable of offering what in certain situations can be counted as a good explanation of facts $F$. (This conclusion is warranted provided that (a) the answers $H$ is capable of supplying could be given in the situations in question in order to render $F$ understandable in those situations; (b) within these situations the answers $H$ is capable of supplying satisfy to a reasonable extent the criteria of evaluation for explanations at a level appropriate to those situations; they satisfy such criteria on the whole better than, or at least not significantly less well than, answers supplied by $H_2,..., H_n$; (c) any other hypotheses that it is reasonable to consider, given $E$ and $B$, supply answers that are inferior to those supplied by $H$, or at least not superior.)

Conclusion 2: $H$ is plausible.

If $A$ explicitly considers alternative competing hypotheses—and this would be indicated by deleting parentheses in premiss 2—we can say that he infers the explanatory power of $H$ from the evidence and the fact that $H$ offers such and such answers to questions while competing hypotheses offer such and such different ones. $A$ will usually consider only some competing hypotheses that it might be reasonable to consider given $E$ and $B$. If so only those he actually considers would be included in premiss 2. If $A$ does not explicitly consider any competing hypotheses—and this would be indicated by deleting parenthesized material in premiss 2—we can say that he infers the explanatory power of $H$ from the evidence and the fact that $H$ offers such and such answers to questions, where he assumes that whatever competing hypotheses there are that are reasonable to consider, given *E* and *B*, do not supply answers that are significantly more plausible. In either case the degree of plausibility assigned to the explanation, and therefore to *H*, will depend upon the extent to which the answers supplied by *H* satisfy the criteria of evaluation and how much difference exists, with respect to the satisfaction of these criteria, in the answers supplied by *H* and those supplied by competitors.

## 4. Other Modes of Inference

Can the explanatory mode of inference I have described be used to characterize all inference to scientific laws? Harman claims that inferences that appear to involve inductive generalizations are special cases of inferences to the best explanations. Since inductive generalizations seem to be involved in the inferences to some laws at least, let me consider this case first.

According to Harman, an inductive inference from 'All observed *F*'s are *G*'s' to 'All *F*'s are *G*'s' is warranted only if the hypothesis 'All *F*'s are *G*'s' offers better explanations of facts than competing hypotheses. If some hypothesis conflicting with 'All *F*'s are *G*'s' offers a more plausible account of the same facts then, even though all observed *F*'s are *G*'s, we are not warranted in concluding that all *F*'s are *G*'s. It is part of Harman's claim that in an inductive inference one infers that a hypothesis *H* provides an explanation, indeed a plausible one, and from this fact one infers *H*. One comes to believe *H* and one's reason for this belief is that *H* provides a plausible explanation. Now, as I have emphasized, whether to classify something as an explanation, and how it is to be evaluated, depends in part on the situation in which it is to be offered. *H* is to be judged to offer a plausible explanation of *q* within some situation *S*. With this in mind, Harman's claim might be understood in one of three ways:

(1) If a person *A* believes that *H* could, in no actual or possible situation, be used to offer a plausible explanation of anything, then he is not warranted in making an inference to *H*, no matter what the evidence.

(2) Anyone who makes an inference to *H* that is warranted does so from the fact that *H* can be used in some situation or other to offer a plausible explanation of some fact, but *A* need not be able to specify the situation or the fact.

(3) Anyone who makes an inference to *H* that is warranted does

so from the fact that $H$ can be used in some situation he can specify to offer a plausible explanation of some fact he can also specify.

Claim (1) is trivial. Any true proposition can be used in some actual or possible situation to offer a plausible explanation of something. If $A$ believes $H$, or that $H$ is plausible, he must believe that $H$ could be used in some situation, actual or possible, to offer a plausible explanation of something. It does not follow from this that when $A$ infers $H$ he must infer $H$ *from the fact that* in some situation or other $H$ could be used to offer a plausible explanation of some fact. Even if we accept (1), it does not follow that $A$'s reason for believing $H$ is the fact that $H$ could be used for explanatory purposes. This leaves interpretations (2) and (3). The former, I believe, is precluded for Harman because he claims that 'in inductive inference one may directly infer by one step of inference only a conclusion of the form $H$ explains $F$'.[1] What the hypothesis explains must be definite. Since Harman does not speak of providing explanations *in situations* it is not clear whether he would say that a situation must also be specifiable by $A$. He should say this if $A$ is really to infer a conclusion of the form '$H$ explains $F$'. For if $A$ can specify no situation at all in which $H$ could be used to explain $F$ then it is unclear what sense it can make for $A$ to assert that $H$ explains $F$. Accordingly, (3) seems the most reasonable interpretation of Harman's claim. The claim, however, strikes me as too strong.

One can make an inference to $H$ on grounds other than that $H$ offers a plausible explanation of certain specifiable facts in such and such situations. The grounds may simply be inductive ones. One may legitimately infer that all $F$'s are $G$'s on the ground that all observed $F$'s have been $G$'s. One may come to believe that all $F$'s are $G$'s and have as a reason for this belief the fact just given. There is one proviso —a point that Harman has recognized.[2] When such an inference is made, generally more is known than simply that all observed $F$'s have been $G$'s. There is a wealth of background information. Given this background information $B$ and the inductive evidence $E$ that all observed $F$'s have been $G$'s, there may be hypotheses incompatible with 'All $F$'s are $G$'s' that it is reasonable to consider as possible alternatives. The inference from 'All observed $F$'s have been $G$'s' to 'All $F$'s are $G$'s' is warranted to the extent that such hypotheses are

---

[1] Ibid., p. 530. I have changed Harman's symbolic letters to conform with the ones used in the present chapter.
[2] 'The Inference to the Best Explanation', p. 90.

not plausible, given $E$ and $B$. The greater the plausibility of a competitor, the less plausible is the conclusion 'All $F$'s are $G$'s'. The plausibility of a competing hypothesis would itself be inferred and the inference could be an explanatory one, an inductive one, or one of any of the other types I shall discuss. (It can be inductive provided that at some point some of the hypotheses considered are inferred on non-inductive grounds.) For example, of the alternative hypotheses worthy of being considered there can be none that implies that not all $F$'s are $G$'s and that, given $E$ and $B$, offers a very plausible explanation of why the $F$'s which have been observed are $G$'s. We can formulate the inductive mode of inference as follows:

### Inductive Inference

Premiss 1: Inductive evidence $E$ is obtained in the light of background information $B$. The evidence is that $F$'s have been examined and all those examined have been observed to be $G$'s.

Premiss 2: ($H_2,...,H_n$ are hypotheses conflicting with 'All $F$'s are $G$'s' that, given $E$ and $B$, it is reasonable to consider as possible alternatives to 'All $F$'s are $G$'s'.)

Conclusion: It is plausible to assume that all $F$'s are $G$'s. (This conclusion is warranted to the extent that (a) hypotheses in the set $H_2,...,H_n$ are not plausible, given $E$ and $B$, i.e. to the extent that no inference is warranted from $E$ and $B$ to the conclusion that such a hypothesis is plausible, and (b) other hypotheses that are reasonable to consider, given $E$ and $B$, and that are incompatible with 'All $F$'s are $G$'s', are not plausible.)

If competing hypotheses are explicitly considered by $A$, we can say that $A$ infers the conclusion from a consideration of the inductive evidence and of certain hypotheses that conflict with 'All $F$'s are $G$'s', in which case the parentheses around premiss 2 are to be deleted and the hypotheses actually considered would be cited in this premiss. If competing hypotheses are not explicitly considered, we can say that $A$ infers the conclusion from premiss 1, where he assumes that whatever competing hypotheses that are reasonable to consider as alternatives, given $E$ and $B$, are not in fact very plausible.

No separate account of variety of instances is needed. We vary instances to rule out competing hypotheses. In determining whether all $F$'s are $G$'s, if we vary the $F$'s with respect to some property $H$— if we observe both $F$'s that are $H$ and those that are not—we do so in order to rule out the competing hypothesis that it is only those $F$'s that are also $H$'s which are $G$'s, and therefore that some $F$'s are not

*G*'s. If no conflicting hypothesis known to those familiar with *E* and *B* is plausible then the factor of variety has been taken into account. This is the best way to do so, since variety is always relativized to competing hypotheses.

What reason is there for thinking that the inductive-inference pattern, as I have characterized it, better describes at least some inferences than the explanatory mode? There are cases in which a hypothesis seems to be legitimately inferred on grounds other than that it offers an explanation. From the evidence that astronomers have always been observed to predict eclipses correctly, suppose I infer, in the light of background information available to me, that astronomers are generally correct when they predict eclipses. My conclusion is warranted to the extent that competing hypotheses that are reasonable to consider, given *E* and *B*, are not plausible. Did I infer the conclusion on the ground that it provides an explanation? I am not aware that I did. What could such an explanation be?

Judging by his response to a similar query,[1] Harman would reply that the hypothesis that astronomers are generally correct when they predict eclipses explains why they were observed to be correct in the past. He claims that this 'does provide a slight though real explanation of their observed success'.[2] What does it explain? The fact that they were observed to be successful? The fact that they *were* successful? Both? Possibly the hypothesis that astronomers are generally correct when they predict eclipses could be used to explain one or both of these. If so, either we would need to imagine special situations in which these could be counted as satisfactory explanations, or we would need to suppose that more is being read into the answer 'because astronomers generally predict eclipses correctly' than might otherwise be thought. In the first case we might need to imagine a situation in which the people for whom the explanation is given believe that astronomers are generally unsuccessful in their predictions and so are puzzled by the fact that whenever astronomers have been observed in the past they have predicted eclipses correctly. For such people the hypothesis in question, together with others, might provide a satisfactory explanation by providing what in chapter IV was called a 'broad' rather than a 'narrow' answer to the question 'Why whenever they were observed in the past did astronomers

[1] By Robert Ennis, 'Enumerative Induction and Best Explanation', *The Journal of Philosophy*, 65 (1968), 523–9.
[2] 'Enumerative Induction', p. 532.

predict eclipses correctly?' The answer would make *q* understandable to those in *S* by modifying and augmenting their views so that the claim that astronomers generally predict eclipses correctly becomes consonant with these views. In the second sort of case we might need to suppose that the answer 'because astronomers generally predict eclipses correctly' is really meant to say 'because *astronomers*, i.e. those who have had years of training and experience in predicting astronomical events, generally predict eclipses correctly'.

Such situations and special readings of hypotheses are certainly possible. But must those who make the inference in question always do so on the ground that the hypothesis inferred can be used for explanatory purposes in such situations or that the hypothesis if understood in special ways can be used for explanatory purposes? This is questionable. No doubt people who infer that astronomers always predict eclipses correctly would assent if asked whether there are situations in which this hypothesis could be used to provide plausible explanations. But it does not follow from this that those who make an inference to this hypothesis do so from the fact that there are such explanatory situations. From the fact that astronomers have always predicted eclipses correctly in the past I infer that they will continue to do so; I am warranted in making this inference to the extent that incompatible hypotheses that are reasonable to consider, given *E* and *B*, are not plausible. But I do not, or at least need not, infer the hypothesis from the fact that in some situations it would, in conjunction with others, and possibly if construed in special ways, provide satisfactory explanations. The mere fact that there is a considerable amount of inductive evidence in favour of *H*, and that of the alternative incompatible hypotheses that might be deemed reasonable to consider none is plausible in the light of evidence and background information, is sufficient grounds for concluding that *H* is plausible.

What arguments does Harman give in favour of the claim that an inductive inference to *H* always involves an inference to an explanation? There are two, the first of which is contained in the following passage:

Enumerative induction is supposed to be a kind of inference that exemplifies the following form. From the fact that all observed *F*'s are *G*'s we may infer that all *F*'s are *G*'s .... Now, in practice we always know more about a situation than that all observed *F*'s are *G*'s, and before we make the inference, it is good inductive practice for us to consider the total evidence. Sometimes, in the light of the total evidence, we are warranted in making our induction, at other times not. So we must ask ourselves the following question: under what conditions is one permitted to make an inductive inference?

... The answer is that one is warranted in making this inference [from 'All observed $F$'s are $G$'s' to 'All $F$'s are $G$'s'] whenever the hypothesis that all $F$'s are $G$'s is (in the light of all the evidence) a better, simpler, more plausible (and so forth) hypothesis than is the hypothesis, say, that someone is biasing the observed sample in order to make us think that all $F$'s are $G$'s. On the other hand, as soon as the total evidence makes some other hypothesis plausible, one may not infer from the past correlation in the observed sample to a complete correlation in the total population.[1]

Harman argues here that we can infer 'All $F$'s are $G$'s' from 'All observed $F$'s are $G$'s' only if the former is, in the light of evidence, a better, simpler, more plausible, hypothesis than competitors; if the evidence makes a competitor more plausible, the inference is unwarranted. To be sure, the example of a competing hypothesis which he cites does purport to explain a certain fact, viz. why we think that all $F$'s are $G$'s. But this competitor, by his own admission, is just one of several possibilities. His argument does not show that the original hypothesis, 'All $F$'s are $G$'s', can be inferred only on the ground that it offers an explanation; nor does it show that competitors, including the example he gives, could be inferred only on the ground that they provide explanations. The most that Harman establishes here is that for an inference to be warranted the hypothesis inferred must be plausible in the light of all the evidence and that no competitor can be more plausible. He does not show how this requires an inference that the hypothesis be explanatory. My claim is that if all observed $F$'s have been $G$'s and if no competing hypotheses worthy of consideration are plausible, given the evidence and background information, then the hypothesis that all $F$'s are $G$'s is plausible in the light of all the evidence.

Harman's second argument is more general. It also purports to show that hypotheses must be inferred on the grounds that they offer explanations. If we are to be said to *know* that $H$ is true then, according to Harman, we must believe that $H$ is true and our belief must be based on a warranted inference. Those propositions on which the belief is based must themselves be true if belief is to count as knowledge. This requirement Harman calls 'the condition that the

---

[1] 'The Inference to the Best Explanation', pp. 90–1. Again I have changed the symbolic letters

lemmas be true'.[1] If inferences are described as inferences to the best explanation, then, says Harman, 'we easily see how lemmas . . . are an essential part of the inference. On the other hand, if we describe the inferences as instances of enumerative induction, then we obscure the role of such lemmas.'[2] Harman supplies an example:

Suppose we come to know that another person's hand hurts by seeing how he jerks it away from a hot stove which he has accidentally touched. It is easy to see that our inference here (from behavior to pain) involves as lemma the proposition that the pain is responsible for the sudden withdrawal of the hand. (We do not know the hand hurts, even if we are right about the pain being there, if in fact there is some alternative explanation for the withdrawal.) Therefore, in accounting for the inference here, we will want to explain the role of this lemma in the inference.[3]

We can be said to know that such a person is in pain only if the pain hypothesis explains the withdrawal of his hand, and this lemma is included, as a premiss or as part of the justification, in an explanatory inference.

These remarks do not provide a knock-down argument against the autonomy of the inductive mode of inference. To begin with, in inductive reasoning, as I have formulated it, it cannot in general be concluded that the hypothesis inferred, 'All $F$'s are $G$'s', is known to be true. The conclusion of the argument is that it is plausible to assume that all $F$'s are $G$'s. (Whether the argument can be said to lead to knowledge of the hypothesis 'All $F$'s are $G$'s' depends on the strength of the evidence, background information, and competing hypotheses.) Even if 'the condition that the lemmas be true' must be satisfied if a hypothesis is to be deemed plausible, it does not follow from this alone that these lemmas have to include a proposition to the effect that the hypothesis offers a good explanation of facts. Since Harman's 'hot stove' example does not involve inductive reasoning from 'All observed $F$'s are $G$'s' to 'All $F$'s are $G$'s', it is not the best sort of example to use to defend his claim that enumerative induction is really a case of inference to an explanation. We might modify the example as follows.

From the fact that whenever anyone has been observed to jerk his hand away from a hot stove he is in pain we infer that whenever anyone jerks his hand away from a hot stove he is in pain. According to Harman, to draw this inference we must assume as an intermediate lemma that 'the pain is responsible for the withdrawal of the hand',

[1] Ibid., p. 92.    [2] Ibid., p. 93.    [3] Ibid.

i.e. that the existence of pain correctly explains this behaviour; for if there is a plausible competing explanation of the withdrawal the inference is not warranted. Perhaps we do in fact assume this as an intermediate lemma, but must we? The inference could still be correct even if we made no such assumption. Suppose we remain agnostic regarding what causes the withdrawal of the hand—perhaps it is the pain, perhaps it is something that causes both the pain and the withdrawal of the hand, perhaps not. To reasonably infer a general correlation between pain behaviour and pain, and to reasonably conclude that one knows there is pain, it is sufficient that there is a past correlation observed and that of hypotheses that compete with 'whenever anyone jerks his hand away from a hot stove he is in pain' that are reasonable to consider none is plausible, given $E$ and $B$. One day we might learn that all the behaviour of some 'people' is caused by signals from an Evil Genius. The Evil Genius causes the feeling of pain, the pain behaviour, and the one to accompany the other, though one is not the cause of the other. If so we could still legitimately infer the feeling of pain from the appropriate pain behaviour, even though one is not responsible for the other, just as we can now infer that a patient has an elevated temperature from the fact that he has measles spots even though one is not the cause of the other.

The inductive mode of inference, as I have formulated it, satisfies the condition that the lemmas be true, if we think of premisses 1 and 2 as lemmas. It does not, however, require that an explanation be inferred, or that a hypothesis be inferred on the ground that it explains facts. Harman's present argument presupposes that the lemmas involved in an inference are always explanatory; it does not demonstrate that they must be.

I conclude that it has not been shown that in using an inductive argument one must infer that a hypothesis provides an explanation. Neither of Harman's arguments establishes this, and the inductive form of inference, as I have presented it, is consistent with what I take to be the valid points Harman does make.

I have considered explanatory and inductive modes of inference. Let me mention several others, the first of which is analogical. From the fact that $F$'s are like $G$'s in having the properties $P_1,..., P_n$, or in having properties similar to these, and that in addition $F$'s have $P_{n+1}$, we infer that it is plausible to assume that $G$'s also have this property or a property similar to it. Such an inference, like an inductive inference, is warranted to the extent that alternative competing hypotheses that are reasonable to consider, given $E$ and $B$, are not plausible. We can formulate this analogical mode of inference as follows:

### Analogical Inference

Premiss 1: Analogical evidence $E$ is obtained in the light of background information $B$. The evidence is that $F$'s are like $G$'s in having properties $P_1,..., P_n$, or in having properties similar to these, and in addition $F$'s have $P_{n+1}$. Alternatively, the evidence $E$ is that $F$'s are like $G$'s in having $P_1$, in addition $F$'s have $P_{n+1}$, and the background information $B$ contains the fact that $F$'s are like $G$'s in having properties $P_2,..., P_n$.

Premiss 2: ($H_2,..., H_n$ are hypotheses conflicting with '$G$'s have $P_{n+1}$', that, given $E$ and $B$, it is reasonable to consider as possible alternatives.)

Conclusion: It is plausible to assume that $G$'s have $P_{n+1}$. (The plausibility of this assumption depends on the extent of the known similarity between $F$'s and $G$'s, on the extent to which $H_2,..., H_n$ are plausible, given $E$ and $B$, and on the extent to which other competing hypotheses that are reasonable to consider, given $E$ and $B$, are plausible.)

If competing hypotheses are explicitly considered by $A$, we can say that $A$ infers the conclusion from a consideration of the analogical evidence and of hypotheses that compete with '$G$'s have $P_{n+1}$', in which case the parentheses around premiss 2 are to be deleted. If competing hypotheses are not explicitly considered by $A$, we can say that he infers the conclusion from premiss 1, where he assumes that whatever competing hypotheses that are reasonable to consider, given $E$ and $B$, are not in fact very plausible. Like induction, the analogical mode of inference does not require that an explanation be inferred or that the hypothesis in question be inferable only on the grounds that it explains facts pertaining to $E$ and $B$. The fact that there are known analogies between $F$'s and $G$'s and that in addition $F$'s have some further property makes it at least somewhat plausible to assume that $G$'s have this property or something like it too, depending on the plausibility of conflicting hypotheses.

There is, however, a type of inference that combines both analogical and explanatory aspects. From (a) the fact that $F$'s are like $G$'s in having the properties $P_1,..., P_n$, or in having properties similar to these, (b) the fact that $F$'s also have $P_{n+1}$, and (c) the fact that $F$'s having $P_i$, one of the properties in the set $P_1,..., P_n$, is correctly explained by appealing to the fact that $F$'s have $P_{n+1}$, it is inferred that $G$'s having $P_i$, or a property similar to it, is also correctly explained by assuming that $G$'s have $P_{n+1}$ or a property similar to it; from which it is inferred that $G$'s have $P_{n+1}$ or a similar property:

### Analogical-Explanatory Inference

Premiss 1: Analogical evidence $E$ is obtained in the light of background information $B$. The analogical evidence (or background information) is that $F$'s are like $G$'s in having properties $P_1,..., P_n$, or in having properties similar to these, and that $F$'s also have $P_{n+1}$.

Premiss 2: The fact that $F$'s have $P_{n+1}$ can be appealed to as offering what in certain situations counts as a good explanation of why $F$'s have $P_i$.

Premiss 3: ($H_2,..., H_n$ are hypotheses conflicting with '$G$'s have $P_{n+1}$', that, given $E$ and $B$, it is reasonable to consider as possible alternatives.)

Conclusion 1: The fact that $G$'s have $P_{n+1}$, or a property similar to it, can be appealed to as offering what in certain situations counts as a good explanation of why $G$'s have $P_i$ or a similar property. (The plausibility of this conclusion depends on the extent of the known similarity between $F$'s and $G$'s, the extent to which $H_2,..., H_n$ are plausible, given $E$ and $B$, and the extent to which other competing hypotheses that are reasonable to consider, given $E$ and $B$, are plausible.)

Conclusion 2: It is plausible to suppose that $G$'s have $P_{n+1}$ or a similar property.

The final mode of inference I shall mention that is relevant in the case of laws is deduction, which I recast as follows:

### Deductive Inference

Premiss: Hypotheses $H_1,..., H_n$ are plausible. (Determining that this is so may involve making inferences of any of the previous sorts.)

Conclusion: $H$ is plausible. (This conclusion is warranted provided that $H_1,..., H_n$ deductively imply $H$.)

In this section and the previous one I have attempted to formulate several modes of inference in a manner that will facilitate a consideration of whether in the case of laws actual scientific reasoning conforms to these modes. Before we turn to this question several issues will require some attention in the following two sections.

## 5. Are these Modes Distinct?

It might be asked whether the modes I have described represent forms of reasoning that are genuinely distinct. There should be no doubt that they do, at least on one level of analysis. This is not to deny that if a person $A$ makes an inference to a hypothesis $H$ via mode $M$, he may have used another mode $M'$ in inferring some of the facts from which this inference was made. Nor is it to neglect the fact that a mode of inference was previously characterized that combines both analogical and explanatory elements. To say that $M$ and $M'$ are not

distinct modes of inference is to say that if $A$ makes an $M$-inference
to $H$ then he is also making an $M'$-inference to $H$, or vice versa. In
accordance with the definition of inference in section 1, this means
that if when $A$ comes to believe $H$ he believes $H$ for the reason given
in $M$ then he also believes $H$ for the reason given in $M'$, or conversely.
But if $A$ believes $H$ for the reason that $H$ is capable of offering a good
explanation of something and competitors are not, this does not
entail that he believes $H$ for the reason that all of $H$'s observed
instances are positive and competing hypotheses are implausible, or
for the reason that $H$ bears an analogy to an established hypothesis
and competitors are less plausible, or for the reason that $H$ is implied
by plausible hypotheses. Nor does his believing $H$ for any one of
these reasons entail his believing $H$ for any other. We must be careful
to distinguish $A$'s believing $H$ for a certain reason from the facts, real
or alleged, which constitute that reason. For example, we must distinguish $A$'s believing $H$ for the reason that all of $H$'s observed
instances are positive and competitors are less plausible from the fact
that $H$'s instances are positive and competitors less plausible. Even
if it could be shown that the latter fact entails that $H$ is capable of
offering a good explanation of something and competitors are not,
this would not show that the modes of inference which appeal to such
facts are non-distinct. The notion of one's reason for believing is
intensional, and if $A$ believes $H$ for reason $r$, and $r$ entails $r'$, it does
not follow from this that he believes $H$ for reason $r'$.

Nevertheless, on some deeper level the distinctiveness of these
modes might be challenged or rendered unimportant if the claim
could be established that one of them is more fundamental than the
others. What might such a claim mean? It might mean of course that
not all of these modes are legitimate or valid, but, e.g., that only
deductive reasoning is, and that other modes become legitimate by
being transformed into this one via the inclusion of missing premises.
I cannot here pursue the topic traditionally called the justification of
induction or non-deductive reasoning, since this would take us far
afield of the present inquiry. Even hypothetico-deductivists, or most
of them, accept the idea that there are valid or reasonable forms of
non-deductive inference. This much should be noted. Unlike many
typical formulations of non-deductive modes the ones I propose have
two elements. All provide some positive reason for believing that $H$
is plausible, e.g. that $H$ offers a good explanation of facts $F$, or that
all observed instances of $H$ are positive ones. And all provide a

negative reason, viz. that alternative competing hypotheses that are reasonable to consider are not as plausible or at least are not more so. Moreover, all of them take into account not simply the immediate evidence at hand but also the background information. My claim is that in each of these cases the positive and negative reasons together provide reasonable grounds for believing that $H$ is plausible; explanatory, inductive, and analogical reasons are valid ones for believing that $H$ is plausible provided that they are considered in the light of the background information and to the extent that competing hypotheses that it is reasonable to consider are not more plausible.

On the other hand, the above claim might mean that the possibility of using any of the previous modes of inference presupposes the possibility of using one particular one; i.e. there is a mode of inference $M$ which is such that whenever anyone uses a mode $M'$ in inferring $H$ from $E$ and $B$, one could also use $M$ in inferring $H$ from $E$ and $B$. This might be construed in a strong sense to mean that although one might make an inference from $E$ and $B$ to $H$ via mode $M'$, provided that it could also be made via $M$, strictly speaking the inference via $M'$ is not valid and should be made via $M$ to be so considered (which, then, would collapse this into the first claim). Or, more weakly, it might mean that although the previous modes of inference are valid, there is one that can be used when any can. With respect to non-deductive reasoning the stronger claim is perhaps one urged by Harman for the explanatory mode of inference. His view seems to be that strictly speaking inductive reasoning, at least induction by simple enumeration, is not valid since it does not include reference to background information or competing hypotheses, a charge that cannot be levelled against the inductive pattern as I have formulated it. In the case of the weaker claim perhaps the most likely candidates for the 'fundamental' mode of inference are the deductive, inductive, and explanatory modes, and these are the ones about which such a claim is sometimes made. To establish the claim one would begin by asking whether one mode is more fundamental than another in the desired sense.

Does use of the explanatory mode in inferring $H$ from $E$ and $B$ presuppose the possibility of using the deductive mode in inferring $H$ from $E$ and $B$? Those who uphold the D-N theory of explanation claim that non-statistical explanations necessarily involve deductive reasoning—a claim criticized in the previous chapter. But even D-N theorists do not maintain that whenever there is reasoning from $E$

and *B* to a hypothesis *H* the latter is deductively implied by the former. At most they assert the converse, that *H* deductively implies *E* and *B* or part thereof. Does use of explanatory reasoning presuppose the possibility of using the inductive mode? In accordance with the explanatory mode, if I infer *H* from the fact that *H* offers a good explanation of facts *F*, which belong to *E* or *B*, does it follow that *E* and *B* contain inductive evidence from which *H* could have been inferred? To answer affirmatively is to say at least that whenever there is explanatory reasoning to hypotheses of the form 'All *F*'s are *G*'s' it is part of the evidence or background information that *F*'s have been observed to be *G*'s. This is to deny the existence of some of the most interesting sorts of theoretical reasoning. I mean reasoning in situations in which observations of *F*'s that are *G*'s have not been made but where nevertheless the scientist infers that all *F*'s are *G*'s on the ground that this hypothesis offers a good explanation of other facts which have been observed or established. Cases of this kind will be considered in the next chapter. Does use of the inductive mode presuppose the possibility of using the explanatory mode? In this case the answer is Yes. As I indicated earlier, if *H* is plausible on the basis of inductive evidence *E* and background information *B* then there is some actual or imaginable situation in which *H* could be used to offer a plausible explanation of some fact, which could be the inductive evidence itself. But this, even if it could be said about explanatory reasoning with respect to other modes as well, only serves to suggest the limited interest of the weaker claim for our main purpose in this chapter and the next, which is to consider the kinds of inferences scientists actually make in the case of laws. By analogy, given various methods for finding the mass of a body, suppose it could be shown that there is a method *M* which is such that whenever anyone uses a method *M'* he could also use *M*. Although *M* might be said to be more fundamental in this sense, this would not show *M'* to be incorrect nor would it show that it is not used. Similarly, if it could be shown that there is a 'fundamental' mode of inference *M*, this would not mean that other modes are incorrect or not employed. (Indeed, the 'fundamental' one, if it exists, might never be employed.)

Another way to construe the claim on p. 134 is this. When one appears to be reasoning via mode *M'* one is really reasoning via *M*. Appearances are deceptive and although it may seem as if people make, say, inductive or analogical inferences, if one carefully examines the situation one will see that their inferences are explanatory.

(Harman seems committed to such a view as well as to the stronger claim two paragraphs above.) This would mean that when people come to believe certain propositions, although it may appear that their reasons for believing them are inductive or analogical, a more careful examination would reveal these reasons to be explanatory. Such a claim is quite relevant to our purposes. In the case of laws our question is whether when scientists engage in reasoning to them their reasons for believing them are genuinely of the various sorts I have described, or whether, despite appearances, they always fall into a single pattern. This question can be answered only by examining particular cases—my task in chapter VII.

## 6. Discovery versus Justification

Many philosophers of science distinguish what they call the context of discovery from the context of justification.[1] Questions pertaining to the discovery of a hypothesis are empirical matters best left to the psychologist. Questions pertaining to the justification of a hypothesis once it is discovered are matters for philosophical scrutiny; it is in this context that the scientist reasons and that his reasoning can be appraised. This, of course, is the view of hypothetico-deductivists such as Popper and Hempel, who claim that whatever psychological processes scientists engage in when they arrive at a hypothesis in the first place do not involve reasoning or inferring but guessing or conjecturing. There is no logic of discovery, only a logic of justification.

This thesis is explicitly denied by Hanson, who maintains that there is a 'logic of discovery', and that it is different from the 'logic of justification'. He explains the distinction as follows. There are reasons for *accepting* a hypothesis *H* and there are reasons for *suggesting H* in the first place.[2] The reasons for suggesting *H* comprise the logic of discovery, the reasons for accepting *H*, the logic of justification.[3]

[1] These terms were first introduced by Hans Reichenbach in *Experience and Prediction* (Chicago, 1938), pp. 5–7.

[2] N. R. Hanson, 'The Logic of Discovery', reprinted in *Science: Men, Methods, Goals*, pp. 150–62.

[3] In a somewhat later article, 'Is There a Logic of Scientific Discovery?', in *Current Issues in the Philosophy of Science*, ed. H. Feigl and G. Maxwell (New York, 1961), pp. 20–35, Hanson modifies this by drawing a distinction between reasons for accepting *H* and reasons for suggesting a hypothesis of the *type H*. Besides introducing difficulties as to how to classify hypotheses into types and how to know when reasons are reasons for suggesting a *type* of hypothesis rather than a particular hypothesis, this way of drawing the distinction is subject to the very same objections that I will raise in connection with the distinction formulated above.

Hanson does not claim that these two 'logics' are mutually exclusive. Some reasons for suggesting $H$ are, he admits, also reasons for accepting $H$, but many are not. What are the reasons for accepting $H$? Repeated observations supporting $H$, new predictions from $H$ which are confirmed by observations, derivability of $H$ from established theories. What are reasons for suggesting $H$ in the first place? The most important, according to Hanson, are 'explanatory' ones: 'Does this hypothesis look as if it might *explain* these facts?'[1] Hanson's 'retroductive' inference pattern is meant to set out this particular mode of reasoning explicitly.[2] Hanson grants that reasons for suggesting $H$ can also be inductive or analogical. The reasons that led Kepler to suggest that all planets travel in elliptical orbits include, among other things, the following: 'Mars does $x$ [travels in an elliptical orbit]; mars is a typical planet; so perhaps all planets do $x$.'[3] According to Hanson, 'these reasons would not *establish* the truth of $H'$ [the hypothesis that all planets travel in elliptical orbits]. Because what makes it reasonable to propose $H'$ is *analogical* in character. . . . Analogies cannot establish hypotheses, only observations can. . . .'[4]

Hanson, unfortunately, has not captured the distinction he wants. Any of the reasons he mentions for suggesting a hypothesis can also be reasons for accepting it, though some will be stronger reasons than others. The fact that a hypothesis offers a plausible explanation of the data can be a reason for suggesting it, but it can also be a reason for accepting it. The fact that mars travels in an elliptical orbit and that mars is a typical planet can be a reason for suggesting that all planets travel in elliptical orbits. But it can also be a reason, though perhaps not a conclusive one, for accepting the hypothesis about all planets. Hanson gives the impression that 'explanatory', weak inductive, and analogical reasons can be reasons for suggesting $H$ in the first place, but not for accepting $H$, which is surely false. Furthermore, the reasons that Hanson cites for accepting $H$, e.g. repeated observations supporting $H$ and derivability of $H$ from established theories, can also be reasons for suggesting $H$ in the first place.

One mistake Hanson makes consists in switching from 'reasons for *accepting* a hypothesis $H$' to 'reasons that *establish* the truth of $H$'. Consider, again, the following: 'Mars does $x$; mars is a typical planet; so (perhaps) all planets do $x$.' Why does this present a reason for suggesting but not for accepting the hypothesis $H$? Because,

---

[1] 'The Logic of Discovery', p. 153.     [2] See above, section 2.
[3] 'The Logic of Discovery', p. 155.     [4] Ibid.

Hanson writes, 'these reasons would not *establish* the truth of *H*. . . . Analogies cannot establish hypotheses, only observations can.' Hanson is surely right that in a reasonable sense of 'establish' analogical reasoning does not establish the truth of a hypothesis, nor does the 'explanatory' mode of reasoning described on p. 123. Yet both certainly provide reasons for accepting hypotheses, though admittedly not always overwhelming ones.

This is not to say that 'reasons for accepting *H*' and 'reasons for suggesting *H* in the first place' mean the same thing. My point is only that whatever type of reasons can fall under the first heading can also fall under the second, and vice versa. Hanson, in speaking of a special 'logic of discovery' gives the impression that although in some cases the types of reasons falling under both headings are the same in other cases they cannot be. There are certain modes of reasoning, e.g. the 'explanatory' mode, that are particularly characteristic of the logic of discovery; they provide reasons for suggesting hypotheses in the first place but not for accepting them; there are other modes of reasoning, e.g. derivation from established theories, that are particularly characteristic of the logic of justification; they provide reasons for accepting hypotheses but not for suggesting them in the first place. This claim, I am arguing, is unwarranted.

How, then, can we distinguish between the logic of discovery and the logic of justification? We cannot, if such a distinction implies a difference in the type of reasoning involved. There is, however, a distinction worth making. If a scientist first came to be acquainted with a hypothesis in the course of reasoning to its truth or plausibility we might say that his reasoning occurred in a context of discovery. If the scientist had been acquainted with the hypothesis before his reasoning occurred and had engaged in the reasoning in the course of attempting to defend the hypothesis we might say that his reasoning took place in a context of justification. Recalling that reasons are being restricted to 'evidential' ones, in the former case there is an inference since the scientist came to believe a hypothesis, and so we can also say that the scientist's inference occurred in a context of discovery. In the latter case there may or may not be an inference, since the scientist may or may not already believe the hypothesis. However, in both cases we can speak of reasoning, and in both cases the type of reason the scientist has for his hypothesis can be the same. The present distinction is by no means exhaustive. A scientist might have known about hypothesis *H* before reasoning on the basis of the data that $H$ is true or plausible, and he might not have reasoned that $H$ is true or plausible in the course of attempting to defend $H$. He might simply have considered the data and reasoned that $H$ is true. If so his reasoning would not fall into a context of discovery or a context of justification. For example, he may be presenting the hypothesis to students in his class and reasoning to its truth even though he has long been acquainted with it and is not attempting to defend it.

Can reasoning involving any of the modes of inference discussed in the previous two sections occur in a context of discovery as well as in a context of justification? The following argument might be given in favour of a negative answer: 'Look at the modes of inference described earlier. With the exception of deduction, each contains in a premiss a reference to the hypothesis whose plausibility is being asserted in the conclusion. For example, the second premiss of the explanatory mode of reasoning contains the statement that hypothesis $H$ is capable of providing a set of answers $S$ to questions con·· cerning facts $F$. This means that someone who is reasoning to the plausibility of $H$ must already have known about $H$ before he inferred that $H$ is plausible. So his reasoning cannot have taken place in a context of discovery, but only in a context of justification or perhaps in neither context. Similar points can be made about inductive and analogical reasoning, as formulated above.'

My reply to this argument is to reject the assumption that these modes of inference require one to have known about $H$ before reasoning that $H$ is plausible. Suppose that while I ponder the evidence and the background information the following thought occurs to me: a certain hypothesis $H$ is plausible because the evidence and background information are what they are and because that hypothesis provides such and such answers to questions concerning $F$ while competitors offer such and such different answers. If this thought does occur to me and if prior to this I have not had the belief that $H$ is plausible then I have made an inference from the evidence and background information, and from the fact that $H$ and its competitors offer such and such explanations, to the fact that $H$ is plausible. I have come to believe that $H$ is plausible and my reason for this belief has to do with the nature of the evidence and the nature of the explanations provided by $H$ and its competitors. It is quite possible for me to have had the thought described above without being acquainted with the hypothesis $H$ at some time prior to that thought. But this means that it is possible for my reasoning to $H$'s plausibility to take place in a context of discovery. That is, it is possible for me first to come to be acquainted with $H$ in the course of making an inference to $H$'s plausibility. On the other hand, of course, $H$ might have been known to me before the thought described above occurred to me, and I might have expressed this thought in the course of attempting to defend $H$. If so, my reasoning took place in a context of justification. It should be evident that what I have said here about explanatory reasoning can be extended to reasoning of any of the modes discussed in section 4. Reasoning of any of these types can occur in a context of discovery, in a context of justification, or in neither of these contexts.

At the beginning of this section I noted that many philosophers deny the existence of a logic of discovery, claiming that reasoning takes place only in a context of justification. Hanson, on the other hand, claims that there is a logic of discovery and that its mode of reasoning is for the most part different from that of the logic of justification. I agree with Hanson that reasoning takes place when hypotheses are discovered and not only when they are defended. But, contrary to what he suggests, the modes of reasoning are the same in both cases. The distinction between discovery and justification, as far as reasoning is concerned, depends not on the mode of reasoning but on the state of knowledge of the reasoner and on his purpose, or lack of it, in reasoning.

We can now turn to the question of whether and if so how the various modes of reasoning so far distinguished are actually employed when laws are inferred.

# VII. Laws and Reasoning

When a scientist reasons to a law does he do so using one or more of the modes of inference so far described? To answer this question I shall examine a number of pieces of reasoning scientists have actually employed in the case of laws. It should be emphasized that a consideration of the pattern of reasoning employed by a scientist is but one element in a study of the origin of a law. Questions could also be raised concerning why a scientist reasoned the way he did, and answers might be offered appealing to his education, his temperament, and his experience. In what follows I am concerned with the reasons a scientist had for believing a law, and with questions of how and why he came to have these reasons only incidentally, in so far as this illuminates the nature of the reasons themselves.

A scientist usually makes several inferences in reasoning to a law. He may make an inference on the basis of facts which themselves were inferred, and he may have arrived at his law using different forms of reasoning. In the first four sections I will formulate one particularly important inference made in the discovery or justification of each of four laws, although there were other inferences that provided a basis for these. In the fifth section a multiplicity of inferences leading to a law will be considered.

## 1. Inductive Inference: Gay-Lussac's Law

In 1809 Gay-Lussac published a paper entitled 'Memoir on the Combination of Gaseous Substances with each Other', in which he formulated the law that gases combine in simple ratios by volume. He begins by pointing out that the force of cohesion between molecules is much greater in solids and liquids than in gases, and varies considerably with particular solids and liquids. Accordingly,

the same pressure applied to all solid or liquid substances would produce a diminution of volume differing in each case, while it would be equal for all elastic fluids [gases].

Similarly, heat expands all substances; but the dilations of liquids and solids have hitherto presented no regularity, and it is only those of elastic fluids which are equal and independent of the nature of each gas. The attractions of the molecules in solids and liquids is, therefore, the cause which modifies their special properties; and it appears that it is only when the attraction is entirely destroyed, as in gases, that bodies under similar conditions obey simple and regular laws.[1]

These remarks provide a theoretical background for the law Gay-Lussac formulated; I will return to them in a moment. In discussing the experimental background Gay-Lussac writes:

Suspecting, from the exact ratio of 100 [parts by volume] of oxygen to 200 of hydrogen, which E. Humboldt and I had determined for the proportions of water, that other gases might also combine in simple ratios, I have made the following experiments. I prepared fluoboric [boron trifluoride], muriatic [hydrochloric] and carbonic [acid] gases, and made them combine successively with ammonia gas, and the salt which is formed from them is perfectly neutral, whether one or other of the gases is in excess. Fluoboric gas, on the contrary, unites in two proportions with ammonia gas. When the acid gas is put first into the graduated tube, and the other gas is passed in, it is found that equal volumes of the two condense, and that the salt formed is neutral. But if we begin by first putting the ammonia gas into the tube, and then admitting the fluoboric acid in single bubbles, there will result a salt with excess of base, composed of 100 of fluoboric gas and 200 of ammonia gas. If carbonic gas is brought into contact with ammonia gas, by passing it sometimes first, sometimes second into the tube, there is always formed a subcarbonate compound of 100 parts of carbonic gas and 200 of ammonia gas. . . .[2]

From the fact, determined by Gay-Lussac and Humboldt, that water is composed of 100 parts by volume of oxygen and 200 of hydrogen, Gay-Lussac inferred that other gases might also combine in simple ratios. His inference was not made solely from the observed fact about the composition of water, but from this in the light of theoretical and observational background information. What was this information?

The theoretical aspect is indicated in the first two paragraphs of the paper, parts of which were quoted earlier. Gay-Lussac indicates that in gases, by contrast to solids and liquids, the force of cohesion between molecules is slight. Because this force of cohesion varies with particular solids and liquids there is no regularity in their expansion and contraction due to changes in temperature and pressure. But in

---

[1] Reprinted in *The World of the Atom*, ed. H. A. Boorse and L. Motz (New York, 1966), pp. 160–70. Quotation from p. 161.

[2] Ibid., pp. 161–2.

gases, since the force is minimal or non-existent, such regularities should exist: '. . . it is only when the attraction is entirely destroyed, as in gases, that bodies under similar conditions obey simple and regular laws.' Because of these theoretical assumptions regarding the uniformity of gases, the number of instances of gases combining in simple ratios that Gay-Lussac needs to observe in order to make a reasonable inference about all gases is considerably reduced. From the fact that hydrogen and oxygen combine as they do, and given theoretical background information, it may be reasonable to infer, as Gay-Lussac did, that 'other gases might also combine in simple ratios'.

A number of other facts formed part of the background information.[1] During his early years as an experimenter Gay-Lussac was the assistant of Claude-Louis Berthollet, whose ideas influenced him considerably. Berthollet worked on problems concerning the composition of the atmosphere. He noted the effect of humidity on the densities of light gases, which made any experiments regarding the combination of gases difficult if weights were to be considered. Berthollet wrote: 'On the contrary, the relationship by volume remains constant despite changes in temperature and humidity, provided that the two gases are under the same conditions.'[2] This emphasis on the importance of the idea of combination by volume is something that Gay-Lussac inherited from Berthollet.

Another fact relevant to the origin of the law concerns Gay-Lussac's interest in the problem of the amount of acids and alkalis necessary to neutralize each other. Before the law of combining volumes had ever occurred to him he had investigated how acids and alkalis combine, but he had not been able to discover any general regularity. His concern with this problem is obvious in the quotations given earlier when he indicates how the gases obtained from fluoboric, muriatic, and carbonic acids combine with ammonia gas. Indeed, according to Crosland, the most important experiments leading to the law were Gay-Lussac's experiments with fluoboric acid and ammonia. It was these that 'led him to repeat very carefully the well-known reaction of hydrogen chloride with ammonia, hoping that the latter reaction might throw some light on the former. These experiments, carried out quantitatively by someone who had

[1] See M. P. Crosland, 'The Origins of Gay-Lussac's Law of Combining Volumes of Gases', *Annals of Science*, 17 (1961), 1–26.
[2] Quoted in Crosland, op. cit., p. 4.

previously made a volumetric study of the combination of hydrogen and oxygen, could hardly fail to lead towards the law of combining volumes of gases.'[1]

If this is right then Gay-Lussac's inference in the context of discovery might better be described as an inference not merely from the simple combining ratio of hydrogen and oxygen, but from this together with simple combining ratios of fluoboric acid gas and ammonia gas, and of hydrogen chloride and ammonia gas, to simple combining ratios of all gases, in the light of background information. Whether the simple combining ratios of fluoboric acid and hydrogen chloride with ammonia should be considered part of the immediate evidence of direct concern to Gay-Lussac, as Crosland suggests, or part of the background information is not of great importance here. What is important is that this provided part of the basis for the inference Gay-Lussac made. Moreover, if Crosland is right these facts were known to Gay-Lussac before the law that bears his name had even been considered by him, and were facts on the basis of which an inference to that law was first made in a context of discovery.

There are other facts Gay-Lussac cited in his paper that provided grounds for the law, but they did so more clearly in a context of justification; they are facts Gay-Lussac invoked after the law had occurred to him, which he appealed to in its support. Thus, in a passage coming a little after the last one quoted above, Gay-Lussac writes:

We might even now conclude that gases combine with each other in very simple ratios; but I shall give some fresh proofs.
According to the experiments of M. Berthollet, ammonia is composed of
100 of nitrogen,
300 of hydrogen,
by volume.
I have found that sulphuric acid is composed of
100 of sulphurous gas,
50 of oxygen gas.
When a mixture of 50 parts of oxygen and 100 of carbonic oxide . . . is inflamed, these two gases are destroyed and their place taken by 100 parts of carbonic acid gas. Consequently carbonic acid may be considered as being composed of
100 of carbonic oxide gas,
50 of oxygen gas.[2]

---

[1] Ibid., p. 25.    [2] Op. cit., p. 163.

Gay-Lussac goes on to cite many other cases in which experiments performed by other scientists ignorant of the law yielded results in conformity with it. He concludes: 'Thus it appears evident to me that gases always combine in the simplest proportions when they act on one another; and we have seen in reality in all the preceding examples that the ratio of combination is 1 to 1, 1 to 2, or 1 to 3.'[1] Here, clearly, is reasoning based on the data Gay-Lussac compiled. When he was writing his paper it was evidently reasoning that occurred in a context of justification.

The question now is which, if any, of the modes of reasoning discussed in the previous chapter best describe Gay-Lussac's reasoning in the context of discovery and in the context of justification? What comes closest, in both cases, is the inductive mode. In a context of discovery, from the fact that hydrogen and oxygen combine in a simple ratio and that various acid gases do so as well when combined with ammonia, Gay-Lussac inferred, in the light of the background information, that it is plausible to think that all gases combine in simple ratios. In a context of justification there is similar reasoning on the basis of combining ratios of other gases. The background information included the idea that gases, because of their molecular structure, should obey simple laws, and the idea, proposed by Berthollet, that combination by volume should be more regular than combination by weight. The first premiss in an inductive argument would include the inductive evidence regarding the combination of various gases and background information of the sort just mentioned. The second premiss would note any hypotheses that conflict with Gay-Lussac's law that he actually considered. Were there such hypotheses?

At the beginning of his paper Gay-Lussac cites a hypothesis, proposed by Berthollet, that compounds are formed in variable proportions. At the end of his paper he agrees with Berthollet that in general this is so, but gases form a special case and 'tend to produce compounds in fixed proportions'.[2] So the hypotheses are not really incompatible, and indeed there is reason to think that Berthollet himself was willing to treat gases as a special case.[3] Accordingly, Gay-Lussac does consider a leading hypothesis of the day which might seem incompatible with his law but, he claims, is really not so. He does not, however, explicitly consider hypotheses that he recognizes to be inconsistent with his law. One of Gay-Lussac's prime

[1] Ibid., p. 165.    [2] Ibid., p. 169.    [3] See Crosland, op. cit., p. 8.

concerns was the discovery of laws, and he was very prone to generalize without careful consideration of alternatives. As Crosland puts it,

A study of his work in these early years reveals that his whole attitude
to research was dominated by a passionate search for laws of nature. Up
to the end of 1808 he had not discovered any new chemical substances, but
he had tried repeatedly to observe and correlate regularities in his experiments.[1]

Gay-Lussac himself wrote:

I devoted myself to research on the expansion of liquids, trying to discover some law . . . Laws are necessarily derived from the observation of
a large number of facts; but, if one were not animated with the desire to
discover laws, they would often escape the most enlightened attention.[2]

If hypotheses that Gay-Lussac recognizes to be incompatible with his
law are not explicitly considered, we can say that Gay-Lussac inferred
the plausibility of his law from the inductive evidence $E$ and background information $B$, where he assumed that whatever competing
hypotheses that might be deemed reasonable to consider as alternatives are not in fact plausible, given $E$ and $B$. One such hypothesis is
that gases combine in many different and complex ratios and that
experimental errors are responsible for the figures which Gay-Lussac
uses. Obviously Gay-Lussac believed that this is not so, although he
did not say so explicitly. (Dalton, who rejected Gay-Lussac's law,
explained the data as being due to experimental error: 'The truth is,
I believe, that gases do not unite in equal or exact measures in any
one instance; when they appear to do so, it is owing to the inaccuracy
of our experiments.')[3]

The question we must now ask is whether Gay-Lussac's reasoning,
either in the context of discovery or in the context of justification,
involved explanatory aspects as well, and indeed is better construed
as explanatory. Did he infer his law from the fact that it offers
plausible explanations? It might be said that Gay-Lussac inferred his
law from the fact that it offers a plausible explanation of the data he
had compiled. It explains why hydrogen and oxygen combine in a
simple ratio, why fluoboric acid gas and ammonia gas do likewise.
The explanation is that all gases so combine, which is Gay-Lussac's
law. As I indicated in chapter VI, a proposition of the form 'All $F$'s

[1] Ibid., p. 11.  [2] Quoted from ibid., pp. 11–12.
[3] Quoted in J. R. Partington, *A History of Chemistry* (New York, 1964), iv. 81.
Dalton rejected the law because he believed that it led to consequences inconsistent with his atomic theory.

are G's' might be used together with other assumptions to explain why particular F's are G's. But we would need to imagine special situations in which the explanation could be counted as satisfactory. For example, we might imagine a situation in which people believe that F's are generally not G's and so are puzzled as to why these particular F's are G's. For such a situation Gay-Lussac's law, together with other propositions, might be cited in order to modify the views of those in S and so reduce puzzlement. Another type of situation is one in which it is not known or realized that hydrogen, oxygen, and the other substances mentioned are gases or in a gaseous state. The question might be raised: 'Why do hydrogen and oxygen combine in a simple ratio by volume (when many other elements do not)?' An appropriate answer would be: 'Because hydrogen and oxygen are gases, and according to Gay-Lussac's law all gases combine in simple ratios by volume.' Other situations might also be imagined in which the law serves as part of an explanation.

When Gay-Lussac reasoned to his law did he do so from the fact that it provides explanations, or serves as part of explanations, of why particular gases combine in simple ratios or in the ratios he cites? There is no evidence of this in his paper. He does not consider situations of the sort just described, or any situations for that matter, in which his law could be used to provide explanations of why the particular gases cited have simple combining ratios or the ones they do. No doubt he believed that his law could be used to provide explanations, or would have assented to this if asked, but there is no evidence that he reasoned to its plausibility on such grounds. There are several places at which reasoning to his law occurs. On the basis of the observed combining ratio of oxygen and hydrogen, together with the background information, Gay-Lussac speaks of 'suspecting . . . that other gases might also combine in simple ratios'.[1] Gay-Lussac here and in what follows mentions nothing about the explanatory value of the law and gives no indication that his inference was based on this. Again, after he lists the experimental results obtained by himself and others, he writes: 'Thus it appears evident to me that gases always combine in the simplest proportions when they act on one another; and we have seen in reality in all the preceding examples that the ratio of combination is 1 to 1, 1 to 2, or 1 to 3.'[2] Again, no mention is made of the explanatory value of the law and no indication is given that Gay-Lussac's reasoning was based on this. Rather, in

[1] Op. cit., p. 161.     [2] Ibid., p. 165.

each of these cases there is reasoning, in the light of the background information, from the fact that certain gases combine in simple ratios to the claim that it is plausible to think that this is so for all gases. More generally, there is no reason to believe that one of Gay-Lussac's motives was to provide explanations. He was searching for regularities in phenomena not for explanations of them. The problem he sets in his paper is 'to ascertain if compounds are formed in all sorts of proportions'.[1] The answer is arrived at by generalizing from instances.

To classify Gay-Lussac's reasoning as inductive is in no way to minimize his achievement. This is not what some philosophers call induction by simple enumeration. Gay-Lussac reasoned not simply from instances but from these in the light of a good deal of theoretical and experimental background information. Moreover, obtaining the experimental data in the first place and then detecting a regularity in his own experimental results as well as in those of others required considerable ability and imagination. Before the law ever occurred to him, Gay-Lussac, together with Humboldt, had conducted numerous skilful experiments with hydrogen and oxygen. Taking into account an impurity of 0·4 per cent in the oxygen, they arrived at a mean combining ratio of 100 parts of oxygen to 199·89 parts of hydrogen, which was rounded off to a ratio of 100 parts of oxygen to 200 parts of hydrogen. According to Crosland, Gay-Lussac's 'predilection for round numbers and convenient approximations dates from this time. The originality of his law lay not in quoting exact experimental evidence, but in generalizing approximations of experimental evidence . . .'[2]

Some writers belittle inductive reasoning as trivial and uncharacteristic of sophisticated science, unlike explanatory reasoning. Coming to believe that all $F$'s are $G$'s may require thinking that is quite sophisticated, whether this involves considering the sorts of explanations a hypothesis and its competitors offer, or considering whether all observed $F$'s are $G$'s and the plausibility of competing hypotheses. Of course, once it has been determined that all the $F$'s observed have been $G$'s, and once it has been assumed that hypotheses incompatible with 'All $F$'s are $G$'s' that are worthy of consideration are implausible, it does not require much intellectual effort to decide whether 'All $F$'s are $G$'s' is a plausible hypothesis. But the analogous point holds true for explanatory reasoning. Once it has been determined that $H$ provides such and such an explanation of the facts, and once it has been

---

[1] Ibid., p. 161.     [2] Op. cit., p. 6.

assumed that competitors worthy of being considered are not as successful, it does not require much intellectual effort to decide whether *H* is plausible.

## 2. Explanatory Inference: Avogadro's Law

In 1811 Avogadro proposed the law that the number of molecules for all gases is the same for equal volumes (under the same conditions of pressure and temperature). What reasoning did he employ? Here is one central argument presented in his paper:

> M. Gay-Lussac has shown . . . that gases always unite in a very simple proportion by volume, and that when the result of the union is a gas, its volume also is very simply related to those of its components. But the quantitative proportions of substances in compounds seem only to depend on the relative number of molecules which combine, and on the number of composite molecules which result. It must then be admitted that very simple relations also exist between the volumes of gaseous substances and the number of simple or compound molecules which form them. The first hypothesis to present itself in this connection, and apparently even the only admissible one, is the supposition that the number of integral molecules in gases is always the same for equal volumes, or always proportional to the volumes.[1]

Substances which combine to form compounds do so in fixed proportions by weight. According to atomic theory this is explained by assuming that it is the molecules within the substances which combine. Avogadro asserts that the relative weights of the substances in the compound depend on the relative numbers of the molecules which combine to form that compound. In view of this fact, one reasonable explanation of why gases combine by volume in simple ratios is that equal volumes of gases contain equal numbers of molecules. For example, given that one molecule of nitrogen combines with one molecule of oxygen to form nitrous oxide, the fact that one volume of nitrogen combines with one volume of oxygen to form nitrous oxide can be explained by assuming that the unit volume of nitrogen contains the same number of molecules as the unit volume of oxygen. Avogadro's reasoning is, I believe, best construed as explanatory. He inferred that his law is plausible on the ground that it affords a plausible explanation, or at least a central part of such an explanation, of why gases combine in simple ratios by volume. At the end of the paragraph, part of which is quoted above, Avogadro writes: '. . . the hypothesis we have just proposed is based on that simplicity

[1] Reprinted in *The World of the Atom*, pp. 175–80. Quotation from p. 175.

of relation between the volumes of gases on combination [i.e. Gay-Lussac's law], which would appear to be otherwise inexplicable.' In a later paper he wrote: 'In my essay on "A Method of Determining the Relative Masses of the Molecules of Substances, etc." I have advanced a hypothesis . . . in order to explain the fact discovered by M. Gay-Lussac, that the volumes of the gaseous substances which combine with one another, and of the compound gases which are produced, are always in simple ratios to one another.'[1]

We might begin to formulate Avogadro's explanatory reasoning as follows:

Premiss 1: Gay-Lussac's law is accepted, as are parts of the atomic theory developed by Dalton.

Premiss 2: Avogadro's law, when taken together with certain other assumptions from atomic theory, is capable of providing an answer to the question 'Why does Gay-Lussac's law hold?' or 'How is it possible for Gay-Lussac's law to hold?' (The answer is given above.)

An explanatory inference will also include within the second premiss mention of any alternative incompatible hypotheses that are being considered. Avogadro does consider a hypothesis that is the contradictory of his and would have to be implied by any competitor, viz. that the number of molecules contained in a given volume is different for different gases.[2] What he says suggests that if this were so and we want to account for Gay-Lussac's law then we would need to invoke laws governing distances between molecules, something we are not required to do under the supposition of his law; moreover, the laws would be more complex than his law. So we can continue to formulate his reasoning as follows:

Premiss 2 (cont.) Furthermore, if it is assumed that the number of molecules contained in a given volume is different for different gases, then any answer to the question of why Gay-Lussac's law holds would need to invoke molecular laws governing distances between molecules, which are not required to be invoked if we assume Avogadro's law, and which would be more complex than the latter.

Conclusion 1: It is plausible to suppose that Avogadro's law, when conjoined with certain assumptions from atomic theory, is capable of

---

[1] Quoted in A. N. Meldrum, *Avogadro and Dalton* (Aberdeen, 1904), p. 16. It might be noted that in the paragraph quoted at the beginning of this section Avogadro concludes not with his law but with an alternation: either the number of molecules is the same for equal volumes or it is proportional to the volumes. The first hypothesis is adopted presumably on grounds of simplicity. It offers the simplest explanation of Gay-Lussac's law.

[2] Op. cit., p. 175.

offering what, in certain situations, can be counted as a good explanation of why Gay-Lussac's law holds. (Avogadro believed this conclusion is warranted because he believed that within those situations his law supplies an answer that is good and indeed better than any that could be offered by competitors.)

Conclusion 2: Avogadro's law is plausible.

In what context did this explanatory reasoning take place? When Avogadro wrote his paper it occurred in a context of justification, since one of his aims in this paper was to defend his law. Avogadro's reasoning did not, however, occur originally in a context of discovery. The proposition that equal volumes of gases contain equal numbers of molecules had been considered earlier by Bernoulli and Dalton, and Avogadro was aware that Dalton, at least, had rejected the idea. Avogadro was aware of the proposition before he inferred that it is plausible.

This reasoning does not provide Avogadro's only defence for his law. Later in his paper he again considers the contradictory of his law, this time because it seems to be suggested by certain experimental results involving chemical reactions in which the volume of a gaseous compound is greater than the volume of one of the gases used in the combination. For example, it was known from experiment that one volume of oxygen combines with two volumes of hydrogen to yield two volumes of water. If we assume Avogadro's law and if $n$ is the number of particles in a unit volume of gas, then $n$ particles of oxygen combine with $2n$ particles of hydrogen. If each molecule of the water that is formed contains one particle of oxygen then there can be no more than $n$ molecules of water formed and hence no more than one volume of water. But according to experiment two volumes of water are formed. In order to deal with this problem Avogadro introduces a second, very important hypothesis, viz. that the particles of elementary gases are formed of several atoms. He writes:

> But a means of explaining facts of this type [experimental results such as the one cited above] in conformity with our hypothesis [Avogadro's law] presents itself naturally enough: we suppose, namely, that the constituent molecules of any simple gas whatever . . . are not formed of a solitary elementary molecule, but are made up of a certain number of these molecules united by attraction to form a single one . . . .[1]

Avogadro goes on to show how this hypothesis together with his law can be used to explain reactions such as the combination of hydrogen

[1] Ibid., p. 177.

and oxygen to form water. The hypothesis inferred is invoked in order to defend his law by explaining certain experimental results which might otherwise be taken to be incompatible with the law. Here as earlier Avogadro makes an explanatory inference, but this time in a context of discovery—the hypothesis of polyatomic gases was not previously known to him.

## 3. Analogical-Explanatory Inference: Inverse-Square Law in Electrostatics

I turn now to a piece of reasoning of a quite different sort, one that involves analogical elements. In his work, *The History and Present State of Electricity, with Original Experiments* (1767), Joseph Priestley describes experiments he performed with an electrified cup:

> . . . I electrified a tin quart vessel, standing upon a stool of baked wood; and observed, that a pair of pith balls, insulated by being fastened to the end of a stick of glass, and hanging entirely within the cup, so that no part of the threads were above the mouth of it, remained just where they were placed, without being in the least affected by electricity; but that, if a finger, or any conducting substance communicating with the earth, touched them, or was even presented towards them, near the mouth of the cup, they immediately separated, being attracted to the sides; as they also were in raising them up, the moment that the threads appeared above the mouth of the cup.[1]

Several other experiments are described. From them Priestley draws a number of inferences, one of which is this:

> May we not infer from this experiment, that the attraction of electricity is subject to the same laws with that of gravitation, and is therefore according to the squares of the distances; since it is easily demonstrated, that were the earth in the form of a shell, a body in the inside of it would not be attracted to one side more than another?[2]

Duane Roller and Duane H. D. Roller provide the following description of Priestley's reasoning:

> Clearly Priestley has used 'reasoning from analogy'. The steps in his thinking may well have been somewhat as follows. There are certain striking resemblances between electrical and gravitational phenomena: (i) both of them involve forces, called 'electrical forces' in the one case, and 'gravitational forces' in the other; (ii) in both cases these forces become weaker as the distance between the bodies is increased; (iii) as shown by Franklin's experiment, the net force between an electrified vessel and an object placed anywhere within it is zero. Almost a century earlier Newton had demonstrated mathematically that the net gravitational force between

[1] p. 731.   [2] p. 732.

the earth, if it were hollow, and an object anywhere within it would be zero. This demonstration was based on the gravitational inverse-square law, suggested to Newton by certain astronomical regularities; his demonstration also indicated that the force on an object within a hollow earth would be zero *only* if the gravitational force between two particles varies inversely with the square of the distance between them. Therefore, since electrical and gravitational phenomena appeared similar in several other ways, it was natural to suppose that they are also similar in that the same inverse-square law of force holds for both of them.

This is just one of a number of instances in which reasoning by analogy or resemblance figured prominently in early electrical discoveries.[1]

If Priestley's reasoning is analogical then perhaps we can formulate it in accordance with the analogical pattern described in chapter VI, as follows:

Premiss: It has been observed that when a small body is placed in a hollow electrified sphere the net force on it is zero. In the gravitational case the same holds true. There is also background information indicating that electrical and gravitational forces are similar in other respects; e.g. they act between bodies separated by a distance and they decrease with the distance. Moreover, in the gravitational case it can be demonstrated that an inverse-square law is operative.

Conclusion: It is plausible to assume that electrical forces obey an inverse-square law.

Does Priestley's reasoning fall squarely into this mould? I believe not. True, Priestley invokes an analogy between electrical and gravitational phenomena, but his reasoning is better construed as including an explanatory element as well. He writes that we can infer that electrical forces are subject to the same inverse-square law as gravitational forces on the ground that the electrical phenomenon he describes is similar to the gravitational case in which the net force on a body in a hollow sphere is zero. By implication, I believe, he is also saying that the existence of a zero net force on a body in a hollow sphere is explained by the existence of an inverse-square force law. He is making implicit appeal not just to the fact that when a small body is placed in a hollow sphere the net force on it is zero and to the fact that an inverse-square law is operative, but also to the fact that one is true because the other is. (Otherwise why mention these facts together?) He then reasons that since there is an analogous phenomenon in electricity, and since electrical and gravitational forces are similar in other respects, it is plausible to suppose that the

---

[1] *Harvard Case Histories in Experimental Science*, ed. J. B. Conant and L. K. Nash (Cambridge, Mass., 1957), ii. 613.

electrical phenomenon is to be explained by the existence of an inverse-square law. We might formulate such reasoning in accordance with the analogical-explanatory pattern described in chapter VI, as follows:

Premiss 1: It has been observed that when a small body is placed inside a hollow electrified sphere the net force on it is zero. In the gravitational case the same holds true. Moreover, there is background information indicating that electrical and gravitational forces are similar in other respects; e.g. they act between bodies separated by a distance and they decrease with the distance.

Premiss 2: In the gravitational case, the fact that when a small body is placed in a hollow sphere the net force on it is zero is explained by assuming the existence of an inverse-square force law.

Conclusion 1: It is plausible to suppose that the electrical phenomenon in question can be correctly explained by invoking an inverse-square law.

Conclusion 2: It is plausible to suppose that electrical forces obey an inverse-square law.

Clearly Priestley's inference was not an inductive one from the fact that in all the cases it is observed that an inverse-square law is operative in electricity to the conclusion that it is universally operative in electricity. Nor did he simply infer the law on the grounds that it offers a plausible explanation of electrical phenomena. The best construction would seem to be that he reasoned to the plausibility of the law on the grounds that a similar law in gravitation provides a plausible explanation of a phenomenon analogous to the one he observed in electricity, and that electrical and gravitational forces are known to be similar in other respects. In what context did his reasoning take place? When he wrote his *History* Priestley was reasoning in a context of justification, but he probably made his inference originally in a context of discovery. Daniel Bernoulli a few years earlier had performed experiments on the basis of which he inferred an inverse-square law for electricity. But Priestley was probably unaware of this since Bernoulli's name is not even mentioned in Priestley's *History*.

## 4. Deductive Inference: Law of Conservation of Linear Momentum

In Newton's *Principia*, Corollary III of the axioms of motion expresses what is now called the law of conservation of linear momentum. It reads: 'The quantity of motion, which is obtained by taking the sum

of the motions directed toward the same parts, and the difference of
those that are directed to contrary parts, suffers no change from the
action of bodies among themselves.'[1] In more modern terminology
the law would be expressed by saying that the total linear momentum,
considered as a vector sum, of a system of bodies comprising a closed
system always remains constant. Newton's reasoning begins like this:

> For action and its opposite reaction are equal, by Law III, and ∴, by
> Law II, they produce in the motions equal changes towards opposite parts.
> Therefore if the motions are directed towards the same parts, whatever is
> added to the motion of the preceding body will be subtracted from the
> motion of that which follows; so that the sum will be the same as before.
> If the bodies meet, with contrary motions, there will be an equal deduction
> from the motions of both; and therefore the difference of the motions
> directed towards opposite parts will remain the same.[2]

Newton first argues that if two bodies moving in the same direction
collide, then, according to his third law of motion, body 1 exerts a
force on body 2 that is equal to, and oppositely directed from, the
force exerted by body 2 on body 1. But, according to the second law,
the change of motion (i.e. change in momentum) is proportional to
the impressed force and is in the same direction as the impressed
force. Since the force body 1 exerts on body 2 is the same in magnitude as that exerted by body 2 on body 1, but opposite in direction,
there must be a change in motion in body 2 that is the same in
magnitude as the change in motion of body 1, but opposite in direction. In other words, one body will gain in momentum what the other
loses, and the total momentum of the two bodies will be the same.
Similarly, Newton argues that if two bodies moving in opposite
directions collide then, since by law III, the impressed forces are
equal, by law II, the changes in motion are the same for both bodies,
but the total motion remains the same. Accordingly, from the second
and third laws of motion Newton derives the proposition that if two
bodies moving in the same or in opposite directions collide the total
motion before is the same as the total motion after.

This is not yet sufficiently general to be the law of conservation of
momentum. For one thing, the law applies to any finite number of
bodies, not just two. Moreover, it applies to motions in any directions, not just to those in the same or in opposite directions. At
the end of his discussion of Corollary III, Newton indicates that in
the latter case the proper results can be obtained by analysing the

[1] *Newton's Principia*, ed. F. Cajori (Berkeley, 1946), p. 17.    [2] Ibid.

motions into components. At any rate, the reasoning above, whose conclusion is the law in a restricted form, is deductive. Newton reasons to his law by assuming that the second and third laws of motion are plausible and by showing how these deductively imply the conclusion in question. The form of his reasoning might be represented as follows:

Premiss 1: The second and third laws of motion are plausible.

Conclusion: *H* is plausible, since *H* is deductively implied by the second and third laws in the manner indicated above.

It should be clear that Newton's reasoning is not explanatory, inductive, or analogical. He was not here reasoning to the law of conservation of momentum on the ground that it provides a plausible explanation of certain facts or of other laws. Nor was he inferring the law from the fact that what it says holds for all bodies that he and others had observed or from the fact that the same or a similar law has been observed to apply in situations analogous to those in question. In writing the *Principia* Newton reasoned in a context of justification. His reasoning was presented in order to defend the conservation law. Whether originally he had reasoned in this manner in a context of discovery is more doubtful. Descartes had earlier formulated a law of conservation of motion, of which Newton was aware, but had not understood quantity of motion as a directional quantity, i.e. as a vector. Indeed, originally Newton may have reasoned to his laws of motion from the law of conservation of momentum, thus reversing the order of the *Principia*.[1]

## 5. A Multiplicity of Inferences: Bragg's Law

In the examples so far I have concentrated on a single inference to a law, or at least a single type of inference, one that might be regarded as particularly central, but each of these inferences was made from facts which themselves may have been inferred. Moreover, a given law may have been arrived at in several different ways, using different inference patterns, and a complete account of the scientist's reasoning would need to include these inferences. In what follows I shall consider the case of Bragg's law, in which several inferences of different sorts were made. My aim is to show how various patterns of inference

[1] See Brian Ellis, 'The Origin and Nature of Newton's Laws of Motion', in *Beyond the Edge of Certainty*, ed. R. Colodny (Englewood Cliffs, N.J., 1965), pp. 29–68.

I have described actually appear in reasoning of a more or less complex sort.

Bragg's law states that when X-rays enter a crystal they are reflected from the crystal only if the following condition is satisfied:

$$n\lambda = 2d \sin \theta,$$

where $\lambda$ is the wavelength of the incident rays, $\theta$ is the angle between the direction of propagation of the incident beam and the parallel planes of atoms in the crystal, $d$ is the distance between these planes, and $n$ is an integer. The law was originally formulated by W. H. Bragg and his son W. L. Bragg in 1912. What reasoning led to its formulation?

After X-rays had been discovered by Roentgen in 1895 the question arose as to whether or not they are electromagnetic waves. It was known that they cannot be refracted or diffracted in the manner that visible light is, so the idea was conceived by Laue to observe whether crystals could produce X-ray diffraction. Crystals are composed of regularly spaced atoms, which should work like a diffraction grating. Experiments were carried out by Friedrich and Knipping who passed a narrow pencil of X-rays through a crystal behind which was a photographic plate. When the plate was developed it was found to consist of a central spot surrounded by a regular array of fainter spots (see Plate I). A reasonable conclusion to draw from this is that X-rays are diffracted by atoms of the crystal, constructively interfere, and so produce the fainter spots. This reasoning is reiterated by the Braggs:

The appearance of the photographs obtained by Laue suggests at once the action of interference. Generally, when X-rays fall on a body which scatters them, the scattering takes place in a continuous manner all round the body. In this case, however, the scattering takes place in certain directions only, and the scattered rays are grouped into separate pencils which leave their impression on the photographic plate in a series of isolated spots as shown in Plate I. The arrangement of these spots shows, both by its regularity and by the form which the regularity takes, that the effect is intimately connected with the crystal structure. It must be connected, moreover, with the fundamental pattern of the structure, and not with any accidental consequences of the crystal growth. For example, in one case the pattern is regular and twofold, and the crystal—nickel sulphate—has twofold symmetry in a plane perpendicular to the direction in which the X-rays passed through the crystal. In the other case the pattern is six-fold: these are the characteristics of the symmetry of beryl in the corresponding plane. It is natural to suppose that the Laue pattern owes its origin to the interference of waves diffracted at a number of centres which are closely connected with the atoms or molecules of which the crystal is built, and are

# PLATE I

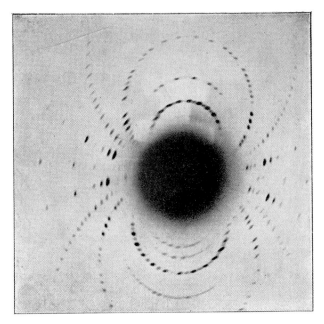

NICKEL SULPHATE

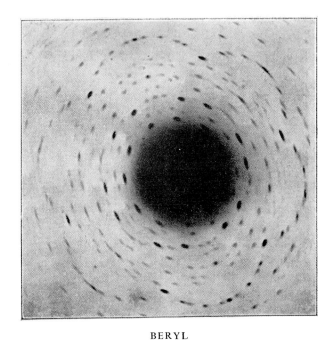

BERYL

From W. H. and W. L. Bragg, *X-rays and Crystal Structure*,
3rd edition, 1918 (G. Bell and Sons)

therefore arranged according to the same plan. The crystal is, in fact, acting as a diffraction grating.[1]

There are several pieces of reasoning in this paragraph. One, to the hypothesis that the scattering of X-rays is due to the crystal structure, is best construed as explanatory. The hypothesis is considered plausible on the ground that it offers a plausible explanation of why the scattered rays are grouped as they are. The evidence is provided by the Laue photographs and there is background information about how X-rays are produced, about crystals, and about the general phenomenon of scattering. A competing hypothesis, albeit somewhat vague, is considered and rejected, viz. that the scattering regularity is connected with 'accidental consequences of the crystal growth'. There is explanatory reasoning to another more explicit hypothesis that the Laue pattern is produced by the interference of waves diffracted at a number of centres in the crystal. This hypothesis is deemed plausible on the ground that, given the evidence provided by the Laue photograph and the background information regarding interference and diffraction phenomena, it offers a plausible explanation of how the Laue pattern is produced. In this case no competing hypotheses are explicitly considered, so we can speak of the reasoning as being made under the assumption that any competing hypothesis that might be deemed reasonable to consider, given the evidence and background information, is not plausible. In accordance with the explanatory pattern we might formulate the reasoning as follows:

Premiss 1: Evidence *E*, the results of the Laue photographs of X-ray scattering, is obtained, in the light of background information *B* concerning how X-rays are produced, the nature of crystals, and the general phenomenon of scattering.

Premiss 2: *H*, the hypothesis that the Laue pattern is produced by the interference of waves diffracted at a number of centres in the crystals, in conjunction with certain other assumptions about crystals, X-rays, and scattering, provides an answer to the question 'How is the Laue pattern produced?'.

Conclusion 1: It is plausible to suppose that *H*, when conjoined with certain other assumptions, is capable of offering what in certain situations can be counted as a good explanation of how the Laue pattern is produced. (The Braggs took this conclusion to be warranted because they assumed that the answer *H* is capable of supplying could be given, in the situations in question, in order to render the Laue pattern understandable in those situations, and that within those situations this

[1] W. H. Bragg and W. L. Bragg, *X-rays and Crystal Structure* (London, 1918, 3rd edn.), pp. 8–9.

answer satisfies to a reasonable extent appropriate criteria of evaluation for explanations, and does so better than those supplied by any
competitors that might be deemed reasonable to consider, given $E$
and $B$.)

Conclusion 2: $H$ is plausible.

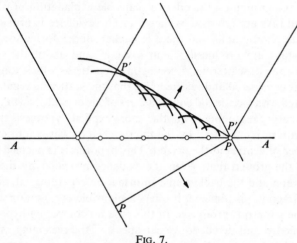

FIG. 7.

Let me turn now to another piece of reasoning the Braggs offer.
The question they consider here is how X-rays are actually diffracted
within the crystal. First they imagine a simple case of a row of atoms
which scatter X-rays construed as waves:

Let us suppose that we have a series of particles which all lie in one plane,
these particles representing atoms or whatever the little obstacles are which
scatter the waves. When a pulse passes over these atoms, each emits a
diffracted pulse which spreads spherically all round it. In Fig. 7 we see the
result of the passage of the pulse $PP$ over the atoms in the plane $AA$. The
circles represent the pulses sent out by atoms in the plane. It is obvious that
all the diffracted wavelets touch a 'reflected' wave front $P'P'$, in fact we
have only repeated Huygens' construction for the wave front reflected from
a plane surface. It does not matter how the particles are arranged on the
plane $AA$, as long as they lie exactly on that plane.
Thus we see that when the pulse passes over a set of particles which lie
in a plane, the diffracted pulses all combine to form a wave front which
obeys the laws of reflection from the plane.[1]

This reasoning contains an analogical-explanatory mode of inference. From the fact that X-rays behave somewhat similarly to light

[1] Ibid., pp. 11–12.

rays with respect to the diffraction pattern produced, the Braggs reasoned that the mechanism producing the behaviour in both cases is somewhat similar. When light is reflected from the surface of a body, as each point of the wave front reaches the surface a spherical wavelet diverges from it. A plane constructed tangent to any such wavelet and meeting the surface of the body is tangent to any other such wavelet. This tangent represents the wave front of the reflected ray of light. (This is what the Braggs refer to as Huygens' construction for the wave front reflected from a plane surface.) Now in the case of X-rays sent through crystals the Braggs are supposing that the analogue of the points on the surface of a body in the case of light are the atoms lying on a plane inside the crystal. Each atom emits a spherical wavelet; the tangent to any such wavelet that passes through the plane of the atoms (*AA* in the figure) is tangent to any other such wavelet. This represents the wave front of the reflected X-ray.

The reasoning might be reconstructed, in accordance with the analogical-explanatory pattern, as follows:

Premiss 1: The pattern produced on a photographic plate when X-rays pass through a crystal is observed to be similar to the pattern produced when light passes through a diffraction grating. There is background information according to which X-rays and light are known to be similar in certain other respects, e.g. both travel in straight lines, they are not charged, both blacken photographic plates, etc. Moreover, a light diffraction grating is similar to a crystal in certain respects.

Premiss 2: The Huygens construction can be appealed to as offering, what in certain situations, can be counted as a good explanation of how a pattern is produced when light passes through a diffraction grating.

Conclusion 1: It is plausible to suppose that the Huygens construction, or an analogue of it, can be appealed to as offering, what in certain situations, can be counted as a good explanation of how a pattern is produced when X-rays pass through a crystal.

Conclusion 2: It is plausible to suppose that X-rays are diffracted in a crystal in a manner given by the Huygens construction or an analogue of it.

Having argued in this manner the Braggs go on to consider various parallel planes of atoms within a crystal. It is the waves reflected from such parallel planes that interfere constructively to produce the spots on the Laue photograph. This argument, which considers exactly how constructive interference works, establishes Bragg's law:

162    *Laws and Reasoning*

So far we have considered the reflection of a single pulse. We may now proceed to consider the reflection of a regular train of waves. Each plane reflects the wave train as a wave train, but when the reflected trains are in the same phase, that is to say, are so arranged that they fit on to each other exactly, crest to crest, and hollow to hollow, the reflected energy is far greater than if this condition is imperfectly fulfilled, even if the want of fit is exceedingly small.

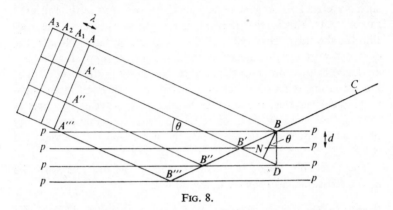

Fig. 8.

Let the crystal structure be represented in Fig. 8 by the series of planes, $p$, $p$, $p$, $d$ being their common distance apart or 'spacing'. $A$, $A_1$, $A_2$, $A_3$,... are a train of advancing waves of wavelength $\lambda$. Consider those waves which, after reflection, join in moving along $BC$, and compare the distances which they must travel from some line such as $AA'''$ before they reach the point $C$. The routes by which they travel are $ABC$, $A'B'C$, $A''B''C$ and so on. Draw $BN$ perpendicular to $A'B'$. Produce $A'B'$ to $D$, where $D$ is the image of $B$ in the plane through $B'$. Since $B'B = B'D$, and $A'N = AB$, the difference between $A'B'C$ and $ABC$ is equal to $ND$, that is to $2d \sin \theta$. Similarly, $A''B''C$ is greater than $A'B'C$ by the same distance, and so on.

If $DN$ is equal to the length of the wave, or is any whole multiple of the length, all the wave trains reflected by the planes $p$, $p$, $p$ are in the same phase and their amplitudes are added together. If $DN$ differs but slightly from the wavelength, say by a thousandth part, the many thousand reflections bear all sorts of phase relations with each other, and the resultant amplitude is practically zero. We see, therefore, that when a monochromatic wave train is allowed to strike the face of the crystal, it is only when the glancing angle has certain values that reflection takes place. These values are given by

$$\lambda = 2d \sin \theta_1,$$
$$2\lambda = 2d \sin \theta_2,$$
$$3\lambda = 2d \sin \theta_3, \text{ etc.}[1]$$

[1] Ibid., pp. 15–17.

The last two sentences above express the law. The reasoning contains at least two elements that fall clearly into the deductive mode, as formulated in the previous chapter. One is the reasoning to the hypothesis that the difference in the distance travelled by two parallel X-rays entering at an angle $\theta$ and scattered by atoms in adjacent planes is $2d \sin \theta$. This hypothesis follows from three hypotheses all accepted as plausible. One, already inferred, is that if an X-ray enters the crystal at an angle $\theta$ to the plane of the atoms it will be reflected, according to the Huygens construction, at an angle $\theta$. Another hypothesis, readily proved from this one plus geometry, is that parallel rays will be reflected at the same angle. A third hypothesis, or set of hypotheses, will be geometrical and trigonometrical ones. These together deductively imply that the difference in the distance travelled by two parallel X-rays entering at an angle $\theta$ and scattered by atoms in adjacent planes is $2d \sin \theta$. The final piece of reasoning to Bragg's law requires the following assumptions which are accepted as plausible: If the distance described above is equal to or a whole multiple of the wavelength of the X-rays, then the reflected waves are in the same phase; if waves are in the same phase, and only if this is so, they will constructively interfere. From these assumptions, together with the previously established hypothesis, it follows deductively that there will be constructive interference of X-rays when and only when the wavelength $\lambda$ of the X-rays is related to the angle of incidence $\theta$ by the formula $n\lambda = 2d \sin \theta$, and this is Bragg's law.

The reasoning involved in arriving at Bragg's law is complex and includes elements that fall into the explanatory, analogical-explanatory, and deductive patterns described in chapter VI. There is explanatory reasoning to one hypothesis which provides the basis for analogical-explanatory reasoning to another hypothesis, and this in turn for deductive reasoning to the law itself. In writing their book, this reasoning took place in a context of justification, in which the law had already occurred to them and in which there were attempts to provide a defence of it. It is also probable that this or similar reasoning occurred in a context of discovery. In one of the original papers on the subject by W. L. Bragg, there is the suggestion that the law was conceived in a context in which there was an attempt to provide an explanation of the Laue pattern that would be more satisfactory than that supplied by Laue himself.[1]

---

[1] 'The Diffraction of Short Electromagnetic Waves by a Crystal', *Proceedings of the Cambridge Philosophical Society*, 17 (1914), 43–57.

## 6. Conclusions

Too often the historian of science concerned with the origin of a law will cite factors that led a scientist to the law but will not pay enough attention to the nature of the scientist's reasoning. M. P. Crosland in his generally informative paper to which I referred earlier considers, as he puts it, 'factors guiding Gay-Lussac to his law'. Although the philosopher of science in reading this discussion will learn some important historical facts about the origin of the law, he will find perhaps a little too much general talk of ideas in the air, or, to use Crosland's term, of ideas that 'converged' on Gay-Lussac's work. Did Gay-Lussac actually reason from these ideas? If so what form or forms did his reasoning take? Did it proceed in a context of discovery, justification, or neither? By appeal to the modes of inference I described in chapter VI, and also by appeal to the distinction between reasoning occurring in a context of discovery and that occurring in a context of justification, I have been attempting to answer just such questions about various laws including Gay-Lussac's.

I have argued that Gay-Lussac reasoned to his law on the basis of an inductive inference; that Avogadro made an explanatory inference, reasoning that his law is plausible on the ground that it offers a plausible explanation of why Gay-Lussac's law holds; that Priestley made an inference that can best be classified as analogical-explanatory in arriving at the inverse-square law of electricity; and that Newton reasoned deductively to the law of conservation of linear momentum. This is not to say that in obtaining their laws these scientists made only a single inference, for they employed assumptions which themselves were made on the basis of inferences. My aim was only to show that one piece of reasoning used, in each case a central one, fits one of the patterns characterized. The case of Bragg's law illustrates how various patterns of reasoning can be involved.

There is a view in the philosophy of science according to which the process during the course of which a scientist arrives at a law is one involving imagination and flashes of insight, not inferences or reasoning. The present chapter and the one preceding it might be thought of as representing a plea for reason. Scientists do make inferences to laws, i.e. they do come to believe laws for which they have reasons. This is in no way incompatible with saying that scientific discovery involves imagination and flashes of insight. There is also a view according to which non-deductive scientific reasoning falls into a single pattern, and another according to which it falls typically into one pattern in a context of discovery and into different ones in a context of justification. My aim in the present chapter has been to consider examples of scientific reasoning that fall into various patterns described in chapter VI. It has been to show that reasons scientists actually have for laws conform to modes of inference previously outlined and that they do so in a context of discovery as well as in a context of justification. I have not thereby dealt with all aspects of the origin of laws, but in formulating modes of inference in a way that permits study of particular pieces of reasoning I have attempted to provide a basis for obtaining one important item of information about the origin of a law.

# Index